Science Notebook

Course 3

Consultant

Douglas Fisher, Ph.D

About Douglas Fisher

Douglas Fisher, Ph.D., is a professor at the Department of Teacher Education at San Diego State University and is a teacher at Health Sciences High & Middle College. He is the recipient of an International Reading Association Celebrate Literacy Award, as well as a Christa McAuliffe Award for Excellence in Teacher Education. He has published numerous articles on reading and literacy, differentiated instruction, English-Language learners, and curriculum design, as well as books such as *Improving Adolescent Literacy: Strategies at Work, Checking for Understanding: Formative Assessment Tools for your Classroom, Productive Group Work,* and *Enhancing RtI.* He has taught a variety of courses in SDSU's teacher credentialing program as well as graduate-level courses on English-Language development and literacy. He also teaches classes in English, writing, and literacy developments to secondary school students.

The *McGraw-Hill* Companies

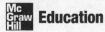 **Education**

Send all inquiries to:
McGraw-Hill Education
8787 Orion Place
Columbus, OH 43240-4027

ISBN: 978-0-07-889438-1
MHID: 0-07-889438-7

Printed in the United States of America.

1 2 3 4 5 6 7 8 9 10 MAL 15 14 13 12 11 10

Table of Contents

To the Teacher

Dear Science Teacher,

As you begin a new school year, one of the biggest challenges you probably will encounter is getting students to read their textbooks. Informational text can overwhelm students, leaving them less likely to read and more likely to become apathetic about learning. I believe that this Science Notebook *will help students use their textbooks more effectively as they learn about science.*

Note-Taking and Student Success

There is considerable research evidence that addresses how students understand difficult concepts and content in school. McGraw-Hill has developed the *Science Notebook* for students based upon that research. Evidence indicates that students need to know how to take notes, use graphic organizers, learn vocabulary, and develop their thinking skills by writing in order to achieve academic success.

The ability to take and organize notes predicts how well students will do in school. Peverly, Brobst, Graham, and Shaw (2003) showed that when students use background knowledge and take notes, they are likely to perform well on tests. Pauk observed that note-taking is a critical skill for college success. Notes serve as an external storage function (meaning on the paper) that builds comprehension and content understanding (Ganske, 1981). This *Science Notebook* is a tool that students can use to achieve this goal. I would like to share some of the features of this *Science Notebook* with you before you begin teaching.

The Cornell Note-Taking System

First, you will notice that the pages in *Science Notebook* are arranged in two columns, which will help students organize their thinking. The two-column design is based on the **Cornell Note-Taking System,** developed at Cornell University. Faber, Morris, and Lieberman (2000) found that the **Cornell Note-Taking System** improves comprehension and increases test scores.

The column on the left side of the page highlights the main ideas of the lesson. This column will help students find information and locate the references in their textbooks quickly. Students also can use this column to sketch drawings that help them visually remember the lesson's information. In the column on the right side of the page, students will write detailed notes about the main ideas and vocabulary. The notes they take in this column will help them focus on the important information in the lesson. As students become more comfortable using the **Cornell Note-Taking System,** they will see that it is an important tool that helps them organize information.

The Importance of Graphic Organizers

Second, there are many graphic organizers in this *Science Notebook*. Graphic organizers allow student to see the lesson's important information in a visual format. In addition, graphic organizers help students summarize information and remember content. I hope that you will encourage students to use the graphic organizers because they will help them understand what they are reading.

Research-Based Vocabulary Development

Third, you will notice that vocabulary is introduced and practiced throughout the *Science Notebook*. When students know the meaning of the words used to discuss information, they are able to understand that information better. Also students are more likely to be successful in school when they have vocabulary knowledge. When researchers study successful students, they find that as students acquire vocabulary knowledge, their ability to learn improves (Martino and Hoffman, 2002). The *Science Notebook* focuses on learning words that are very specific to understanding the content of the textbook. The *Science Notebook* also highlights general academic words that students need to know so that they can understand any textbook. These vocabulary words are based on the Academic Word List (AWL) developed by Averil Coxhead. The AWL includes the most common 570 words found in academic texts, excluding the 2,000 general English words such as *the*, *in*, and *that*. Research indicates that students who master the words on Coxhead's list score significantly higher on standardized tests.

Writing Prompts and Note-Taking

Finally, there are a number of writing exercises included in this *Science Notebook*. Writing is a useful tool that helps students understand the information that is being presented. Writing helps them to assess what they have learned. You will see that many of the writing exercises require students to practice the skills of good readers. Good readers *make connections* between their lives and the text. They question the information, *clarify* information and ideas, and *visualize* what is described in the text. Good readers also *summarize* the information that is presented and *make inferences* or *draw conclusions* about the facts and ideas.

I wish you well as you begin another school year. This *Science Notebook* is designed to help students understand the information in your science class. The guide will be a valuable tool that also will provide students with skills that they can use throughout their lives.

I hope you have a successful school year.

Sincerely,

Douglas Fisher

References

Faber, J.E., Morris, J.D., and Lieberman, M.G. (2000). The effect of note taking on ninth grade students' comprehension. *Reading Psychology,* 21, 257–270.

Ganske, L. (1981). Note-taking: A significant and integral part of learning environments. *Educational Communication and Technology: A Journal of Theory, Research, and Development,* 29, 155–175.

Martino, N. L., and Hoffman, P.R. (2002). An investigation of reading and language abilities of college freshmen. *Journal of Research in Reading,* 25 310–318.

Pauk, W. (1974). How to Study in College. Boston: Houghton Mifflin.

Peverly, S.T., Brobst, K.E., Graham, M., Shaw, R. (2003). College adults are not good a self-regulation: A study on the relationship of self-regulation , note-taking, and test taking. *Journal of Educational Psychology,* 95, 335–346.

Van Leeuwe, J., and Aarnouise, C. (1998). Relation between reading comprehension, vocabulary, reading pleasure, and reading frequency. *Educational Research and Evaluation,* 4, 143–166.

Using Your Science Notebook

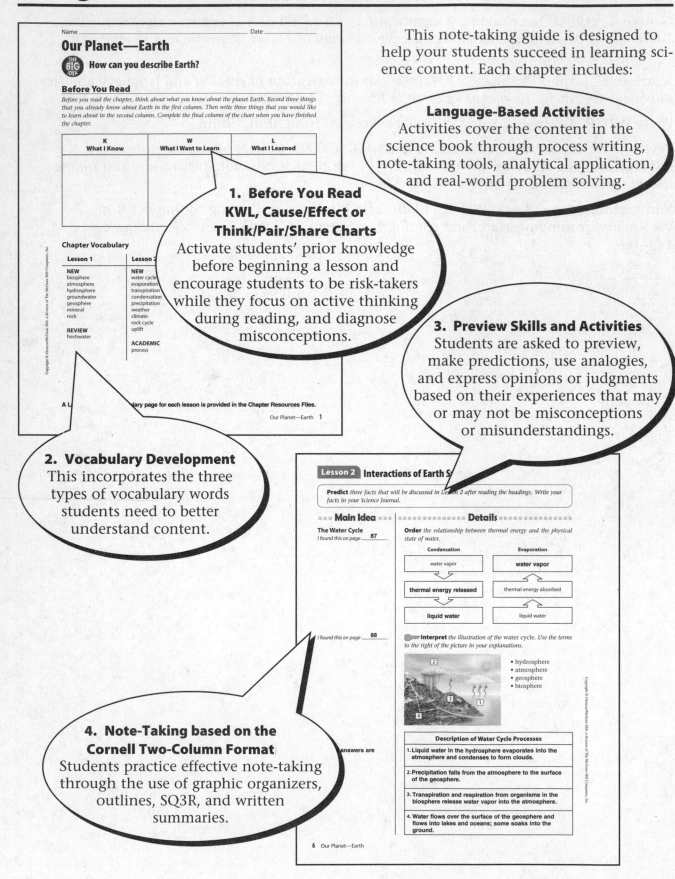

This note-taking guide is designed to help your students succeed in learning science content. Each chapter includes:

Language-Based Activities
Activities cover the content in the science book through process writing, note-taking tools, analytical application, and real-world problem solving.

**1. Before You Read
KWL, Cause/Effect or
Think/Pair/Share Charts**
Activate students' prior knowledge before beginning a lesson and encourage students to be risk-takers while they focus on active thinking during reading, and diagnose misconceptions.

3. Preview Skills and Activities
Students are asked to preview, make predictions, use analogies, and express opinions or judgments based on their experiences that may or may not be misconceptions or misunderstandings.

2. Vocabulary Development
This incorporates the three types of vocabulary words students need to better understand content.

4. Note-Taking based on the Cornell Two-Column Format
Students practice effective note-taking through the use of graphic organizers, outlines, SQ3R, and written summaries.

5. Graphic Organizers

These organizers offer a variety of effective ways to organize, analyze, and summarize information; remember content and ensure learning and understanding for all students.

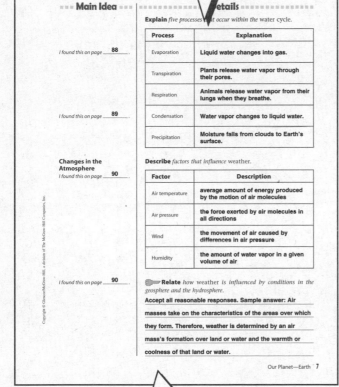

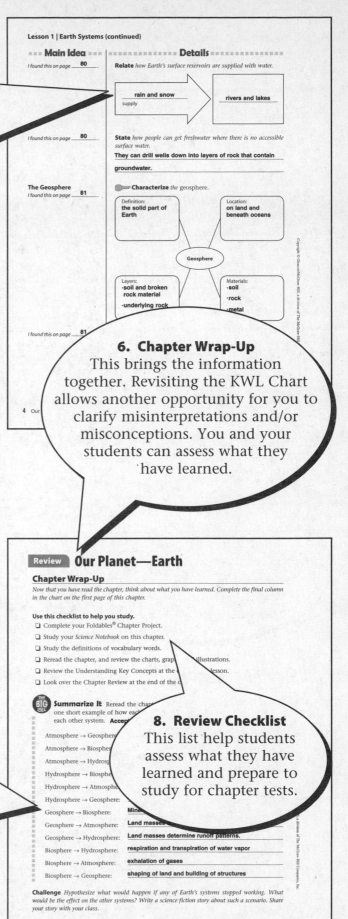

Main Idea

I found this on page ___ 80

Details

Relate how Earth's surface reservoirs are supplied with water.

rain and snow

supply → rivers and lakes

I found this on page ___ 80

State how people can get freshwater where there is no accessible surface water.

They can drill wells down into layers of rock that contain groundwater.

The Geosphere
I found this on page ___ 81

Characterize the geosphere.

Definition:
the solid part of Earth

Location:
on land and beneath oceans

Geosphere

Layers:
·soil and broken rock material
·underlying rock

Materials:
·soil
·rock
·metal

I found this on page ___ 81

6. Chapter Wrap-Up

This brings the information together. Revisiting the KWL Chart allows another opportunity for you to clarify misinterpretations and/or misconceptions. You and your students can assess what they have learned.

4   Our

Main Idea

Details

Explain five processes that occur within the water cycle.

Process	Explanation
Evaporation	Liquid water changes into gas.
Transpiration	Plants release water vapor through their pores.
Respiration	Animals release water vapor from their lungs when they breathe.
Condensation	Water vapor changes to liquid water.
Precipitation	Moisture falls from clouds to Earth's surface.

I found this on page ___ 88

I found this on page ___ 89

Changes in the Atmosphere
I found this on page ___ 90

Describe factors that influence weather.

Factor	Description
Air temperature	average amount of energy produced by the motion of air molecules
Air pressure	the force exerted by air molecules in all directions
Wind	the movement of air caused by differences in air pressure
Humidity	the amount of water vapor in a given volume of air

I found this on page ___ 90

Relate how weather is influenced by conditions in the geosphere and the hydrosphere.

Accept all reasonable responses. Sample answer: Air masses take on the characteristics of the areas over which they form. Therefore, weather is determined by an air mass's formation over land or water and the warmth or coolness of that land or water.

Our Planet—Earth   **7**

7. Writing Activities

Research shows that these activities help students' process information and make connections between concepts and the real world as they strengthen scientific writing skills and metacognition.

Review   **Our Planet—Earth**

Chapter Wrap-Up

Now that you have read the chapter, think about what you have learned. Complete the final column in the chart on the first page of this chapter.

Use this checklist to help you study.
- [ ] Complete your Foldables® Chapter Project.
- [ ] Study your *Science Notebook* on this chapter.
- [ ] Study the definitions of vocabulary words.
- [ ] Reread the chapter, and review the charts, graphs, illustrations.
- [ ] Review the Understanding Key Concepts at the ... lesson.
- [ ] Look over the Chapter Review at the end of the ...

Summarize It Reread the chapter ... one short example of how each ... each other system. Accept ...

Atmosphere → Geosphere:
Atmosphere → Biosphere:
Atmosphere → Hydrosphere:
Hydrosphere → Biosphere:
Hydrosphere → Atmosphere:
Hydrosphere → Geosphere:
Geosphere → Biosphere: Mine...
Geosphere → Atmosphere: Land masses...
Geosphere → Hydrosphere: Land masses determine runoff patterns.
Biosphere → Hydrosphere: respiration and transpiration of water vapor
Biosphere → Atmosphere: exhalation of gases
Biosphere → Geosphere: shaping of land and building of structures

Challenge Hypothesize what would happen if any of Earth's systems stopped working. What would be the effect on the other systems? Write a science fiction story about such a scenario. Share your story with your class.

10   Our Planet—Earth

8. Review Checklist

This list help students assess what they have learned and prepare to study for chapter tests.

Name _____ Date _____

Scientific Problem Solving

 What is scientific inquiry?

Before You Read

Before you read the chapter, think about what you know about science and how it is carried out. Record three things that you already know about scientific inquiry. Then write three things that you would like to learn about in the second column. Complete the final column of the chart when you have finished the chapter.

K What I Know	W What I Want to Learn	L What I Learned

Chapter Vocabulary

Lesson 1	Lesson 2	Lesson 3
NEW science observation inference hypothesis prediction scientific theory scientific law technology critical thinking	**NEW** description explanation International System of Units (SI) scientific notation percent error	**NEW** variable independent variable dependent variable constants qualitative data quantitative data experimental group control group

A Lesson Content Vocabulary page for each lesson is provided in the Chapter Resources Files.

> **Predict** *three facts that will be discussed in Lesson 1 after reading the headings. Record your predictions in your Science Journal.*

▪▪▪ **Main Idea** ▪▪▪ | ▪▪▪▪▪▪ **Details** ▪▪▪▪▪▪

Understanding Science
I found this on page NOS 4 .

Characterize science.

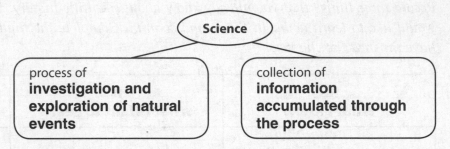

Branches of Science
I found this on page NOS 5 .

Describe *the areas of study of three branches of* science.

Branch	Description
Physical science	the study of matter and energy
Earth science	the study of the many processes that occur on Earth
Life science	the study of all organisms and the processes that occur in them

What is Scientific Inquiry?
I found this on page NOS 6 .

Differentiate *terms that apply to scientific inquiry.*

Observation using one or more of your senses to gather information	Inference a logical explanation of an observation	Hypothesis a possible explanation for an observation that can be tested by scientific investigations

I found this on page NOS 7 .

Relate *the importance of testing a* hypothesis.

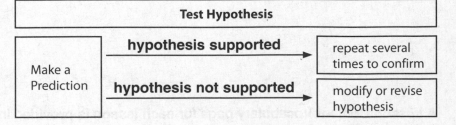

▪▪▪ **Main Idea** ▪▪▪ | ▪▪▪▪▪▪▪▪▪ **Details** ▪▪▪▪▪▪▪▪▪

Scientific Theory and Scientific Law

I found this on page ___NOS 8___.

Compare and contrast *a scientific theory* with *a scientific law.*

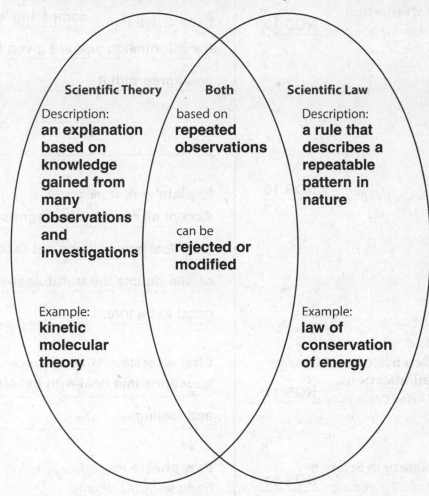

Scientific Theory

Description:
an explanation based on knowledge gained from many observations and investigations

Example:
kinetic molecular theory

Both

based on
repeated observations

can be
rejected or modified

Scientific Law

Description:
a rule that describes a repeatable pattern in nature

Example:
law of conservation of energy

Results of Scientific Inquiry

I found this on page ___NOS 9___.

🔑 **Classify** *results of scientific inquiry.*

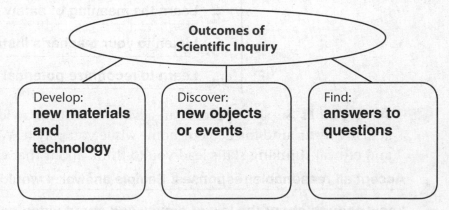

Outcomes of Scientific Inquiry

Develop:
new materials and technology

Discover:
new objects or events

Find:
answers to questions

I found this on page ___NOS 9___.

Define technology.

Technology: __the practical use of scientific knowledge,__

__especially for industrial or commercial use__

■■■ **Main Idea** ■■■ | ■■■■■■■■■■■ **Details** ■■■■■■■■■■■■■

Evaluating Scientific Information
I found this on page __NOS 10__ .

🔑 **Point out** *the skills used in* critical thinking.
Critical Thinking: __comparing what you already know with__ __the information you are given in order to decide whether__ __you agree with it__

I found this on page __NOS 10__ .

Explain *what it means to be skeptical.*
__Accept all reasonable responses. Sample answer: A__ __skeptical person does not take everything at face value. He__ __or she doubts the truthfulness of things that sound too__ __good to be true.__

Science cannot answer all questions.
I found this on page __NOS 11__ .

Characterize *questions that cannot be answered scientifically.*
__questions that deal with beliefs, values, personal opinions,__ __and feelings__

Safety in Science
I found this on page __NOS 11__ .

Paraphrase *four safety practices you should always use when you begin scientific inquiry.*
1. __Wear protective equipment.__
2. __Learn the meaning of safety symbols.__
3. __Listen to your teacher's instructions.__
4. __Learn to recognize potential hazards.__

🔑 **Analyze It** Suppose you see an advertisement for a video game that claims you can actually fly around inside your home while you play it. What do your scientific literacy and critical thinking skills lead you to think about that claim?

__Accept all reasonable responses. Sample answer: I would not believe it, because I__ __know enough about the law of gravity and about video game technology to be very__ __skeptical about a claim that a game can make me fly in my home.__

Scan *Lesson 2. Read the lesson titles and bold words. Look at the pictures. Identify three facts you discovered about measurement and scientific tools. Record your facts in your Science Journal.*

▪▪▪ **Main Idea** ▪▪▪

▪▪▪▪▪ **Details** ▪▪▪▪▪

Description and Explanation

I found this on page __NOS 12__ .

Compare and contrast descriptions *and* explanations.

Description spoken or written summary	Both have to do with observations	Explanation interpretation of observations

The International System of Units

I found this on page __NOS 12__ .

🔑 **Identify** *the problem solved by the development of the International System of Units (SI).*

| Problem confusion among people using different measurements in different parts of the world | Solution adoption by scientists of the International System of Units

Definition: **the internationally accepted system of measurement** |
|---|---|

I found this on page __NOS 13__ .

Interpret *the meaning of* SI *measurements.*

Measurement	Prefix	Meaning of Prefix	Quantity Measured
kilometer	**kilo-**	**1,000**	length
millisecond	**milli-**	**1/1,000**	time
microgram	**micro-**	**1/1,000,000**	mass

I found this on page __NOS 13__ .

Identify *the SI units for these measurements.*

Quantity Measured	Unit and Symbol	Quantity Measured	Unit and Symbol
Electric current	**ampere, A**	Substance amount	**mole, mol**
Temperature	**Kelvin, K**	Light intensity	**candela, cd**

■■■■ **Main Idea** ■■■■ | ■■■■■■■■■■■■■■■ **Details** ■■■■■■■■■■■■■■■

Measurement and Uncertainty
I found this on page __NOS 14__ .

Model *accuracy and precision. The "bull's-eye" represents an accepted value.*

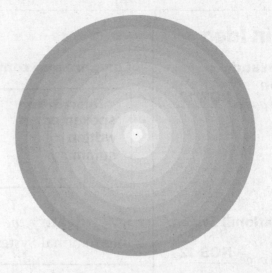

Drawings should reflect the following explanations:

Draw	Explain
Three red dots that are both accurate and precise	**measurements close to each other *and* near the bull's eye (the accepted value)**
One blue dot that is accurate	**measurement in the bull's-eye, right on the accepted value**
Three green dots that are neither accurate nor precise	**measurements neither close to each other nor to the accepted value; scattered dots not near the bull's eye**
Three black dots that are precise but not accurate	**measurements close to each other but not close to the accepted value (bull's eye)**

▪▪▪ **Main Idea** ▪▪▪ | ▪▪▪▪▪▪▪▪▪▪▪▪▪▪▪ **Details** ▪▪▪▪▪▪▪▪▪▪▪▪▪▪▪

I found this on page __NOS 14__ .

Relate *the precision of tools to certainty.*

| Tools with __greater__ precision | provide measurements with | → | __more__ certainty. |

| Tools with __less__ precision | provide measurements with | → | __less__ certainty. |

I found this on page __NOS 15__ .

 Assess *the usefulness of* scientific notation.

Scientific notation, the method of displaying very large and

very small numbers, takes up less writing space.

_____

_____

I found this on page __NOS 15__ .

Express *each value in* scientific notation.

Number	In Scientific Notation
234,000	2.34×10^5
.00067	6.7×10^{-4}
842,700,000,000	8.427×10^{11}
.0000000111	1.11×10^{-8}

I found this on page __NOS 15__ .

Restate *the* percent error *equation.*

$$\text{percent error} = \frac{|\text{experimental value} - \text{accepted value}|}{\text{accepted value}} \times 100\%$$

▪▪▪ **Main Idea** ▪▪▪ | ▪▪▪▪▪▪▪▪▪▪▪ **Details** ▪▪▪▪▪▪▪▪▪▪▪

Scientific Tools
I found this on page __NOS 16__ .

⚷ **Identify** *the uses of six scientific tools.*

Tool	Description of Use
Science journal	**to record observations, questions, hypotheses, data, and results**
Balance	**to measure the masses of objects**
Glassware	**to hold or measure liquids**
Thermometer	**to measure the temperature of substances**
Calculator	**to make quick calculations using data**
Computer	**to collect, compile, and analyze data**

I found this on page __NOS 17__ .

Additional Tools Used by Physical Scientists
I found this on page __NOS 18__ .

⚷ **Describe** *how physical scientists use these tools.*

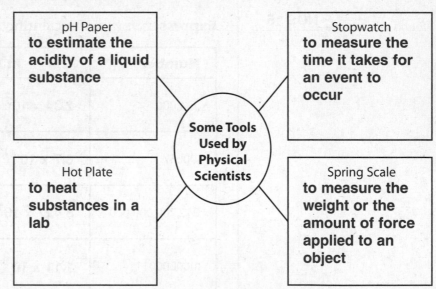

pH Paper
to estimate the acidity of a liquid substance

Stopwatch
to measure the time it takes for an event to occur

Hot Plate
to heat substances in a lab

Some Tools Used by Physical Scientists

Spring Scale
to measure the weight or the amount of force applied to an object

⚷ **Connect It** In November you notice that it seems to be darker in the morning when you are getting ready for school. How can you use tools to make your observation more scientific and evaluate it?

Accept all reasonable responses. Sample answer: I can observe what time it gets

light each morning for several weeks and record the observations in a science

journal. Then I can compare and analyze the data and draw a conclusion from it.

Lesson 3 | Case Study

Skim *Lesson 3 in your book. Read the headings and look at the photos and illustrations. Identify three things you want to learn more about as you read the lesson. Record your ideas in your Science Journal.*

■■■ Main Idea ■■■ | ■■■■■ Details ■■■■■

The Minneapolis Bridge Failure
I found this on page ___NOS 20___ .

🔑 **Predict** *how scientific inquiry could be used to investigate a bridge failure.*

Accept all reasonable responses. Sample answer:

Investigators could review the bridge's design and the

debris from the collapse, hypothesize reasons for the

failure, and then make and test their hypotheses.

Controlled Experiments
I found this on page ___NOS 21___ .

Define *parts of a controlled experiment.*

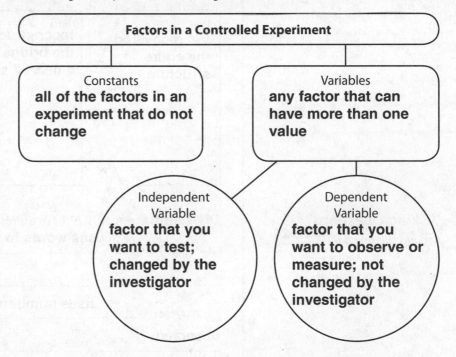

Factors in a Controlled Experiment

Constants
all of the factors in an experiment that do not change

Variables
any factor that can have more than one value

Independent Variable
factor that you want to test; changed by the investigator

Dependent Variable
factor that you want to observe or measure; not changed by the investigator

I found this on page ___NOS 21___ .

Relate *groups in a controlled experiment.*

Experimental Group
used to study how a change in the independent variable changed the dependent variable

Control Group
contains the same factors as the experimental group, but the independent variable is not changed

▪▪▪ Main Idea ▪▪▪ | ▪▪▪▪▪▪ Details ▪▪▪▪▪▪

Simple Beam Bridges and Truss Bridges

I found this on page __NOS 21__ .

I found this on page __NOS 22__ .

Compare and contrast *a simple beam bridge and a truss bridge.*

simple beam bridge: has only one horizontal beam across two supports

truss bridge: also is supported only at its two ends, but an assembly of interconnected triangles, or trusses, strengthens it

Bridge Failure Observations

I found this on page __NOS 23__ .

🔑 **Order** *the evaluation of the bridge collapse.*

Rescuing and recovering victims was the first priority.

Investigators then **recovered the entire structure**

and **reconstructed the bridge at a nearby site.**

They also found clues **in videos that revealed the sequence of the bridge collapse.**

Asking Questions
I found this on page __NOS 24__ .

Differentiate *ways that variables can be observed.*

qualitative data: uses words to describe what is observed

quantitative data: uses numbers to describe what is observed

I found this on page __NOS 24__ .

🔑 **Record** *an early hypothesis formed by investigators of the bridge collapse.*

Hypothesis: **The bridge failed because it was overloaded.**

Lesson 3 | Case Study (continued)

■■■ **Main Idea** ■■■ | ■ ■ ■ ■ ■ ■ ■ **Details** ■ ■ ■ ■ ■ ■ ■ ■ ■ ■ ■

I found this on page __NOS 25__ .   **Identify** *the method investigators used to rule out overloading as the cause of the bridge collapse.*

computer modeling

I found this on page __NOS 25__ .   🔑 **Paraphrase** *investigators' revised hypothesis about the cause of the bridge collapse.*

> Revised hypothesis: **Gusset plates failed, which led to the bridge collapse.**

I found this on page __NOS 26__ .   🔑 **Sequence** *the data analysis that led to the conclusion about the bridge's collapse.*

> Investigators determined the demand-to-capacity ratio for the whole bridge structure.

> **They calculated the demand-to-capacity ratio for each of the main gusset plates.**

> **The demand-to-capacity ratio at node U10 was too high, and that plate failed first.**

I found this on page __NOS 27__ .   **Infer** *the importance of publishing the results of scientific testing and analysis.*

The reports provide scientists and engineers with valuable

information they can use in future designs and testing.

🔑 **Synthesize It** Summarize the conclusion investigators made about the reasons for the bridge collapse in the case study in Lesson 3.

Accept all reasonable responses. Sample answer: The collapse was caused by

undersized gusset plates, along with added, concentrated load from construction

vehicles and materials.

Chapter Wrap-Up

Now that you have read the chapter, think about what you have learned. Complete the final column of the chart on the first page.

Use this checklist to help you study.

❏ Complete your Foldables® Chapter Project.

❏ Study your *Science Notebook* on this chapter.

❏ Study the definitions of vocabulary words.

❏ Reread the chapter, and review the charts, graphs, and illustrations.

❏ Review the Understanding Key Concepts at the end of each lesson.

❏ Look over the Chapter Review at the end of the chapter.

THE BIG IDEA **Summarize It** Reread the chapter Big Idea and the lesson Key Concepts. Summarize how the bridge case study described in Lesson 3 shows the application of Key Concepts from Lessons 1 and 2.

Accept all reasonable responses. Sample answer: The Key Concepts in Lesson 1

are about what science is and how the process of scientific inquiry is conducted.

The bridge case study in Lesson 3 describes examples of how scientists pieced

together evidence from an accident, made observations and measurements of those

pieces, and were able to draw conclusions from the data. The Key Concepts of

Lesson 2 center on how and why scientists make and record accurate and precise

measurements during their investigations. By using these mathematical models and

understanding margins of error, the scientists in the Lesson 3 case study could rule

out some possible causes of the bridge collapse and modify and test other

hypotheses.

Challenge *Choose another type of bridge construction to learn about. Build a small model of that type of bridge and label your model with captions that explain how the design works to carry the bridge's loads. Test your model. Display your model and the test results in your classroom.*

Describing Motion

 What are some ways to describe motion?

Before You Read

Before you read the chapter, think about what you know about motion. Record your thoughts in the first column. Pair with a partner, and discuss his or her thoughts. Write those thoughts in the second column. Then record what you both would like to share with the class in the third column.

Think	Pair	Share

Chapter Vocabulary

Lesson 1	Lesson 2	Lesson 3
NEW reference point position motion displacement	**NEW** speed constant speed instantaneous speed average speed velocity	**NEW** acceleration average acceleration
ACADEMIC specify		
REVIEW dimension		

A Lesson Content Vocabulary page for each lesson is provided in the Chapter Resources Files.

Position and Motion

> **Scan** *Lesson 1. Read the lesson titles and bold words. Look at the pictures. Identify three facts that you discovered about position and motion. Write your facts in your Science Journal.*

■■■ **Main Idea** ■■■

Describing Position
I found this on page _____9_____ .

I found this on page _____10_____ .

I found this on page _____11_____ .

■■■■■■■■■ **Details** ■■■■■■■■■

🔑➡ **Explain** *how a reference point is used to describe* position.

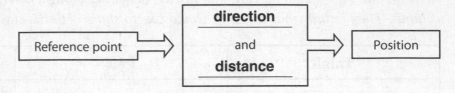

Identify *what must change if the* reference point *is changed.*

When a reference point is changed, the description of the _____direction_____ and the _____distance_____ to the object also must be changed.

Find *each building's reference direction and distance. West is the specified reference direction. Then use a reference point and the distance to give directions from the post office to the mall.*

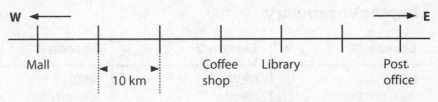

	Reference Direction	**Distance (km)**
Mall to post office	negative	60 km
Library to coffee shop	positive	10 km
Mall to library	negative	40 km
Post office to coffee shop	positive	30 km

Directions: **Travel west 60 km past the library and/or the coffee shop.**

▪▪▪ **Main Idea** ▪▪▪ ▪▪▪▪▪▪▪▪▪▪▪▪ **Details** ▪▪▪▪▪▪▪▪▪▪▪▪

Describing Position in Two Dimensions

I found this on page ___12___ .

🔑 **Sequence** *the steps in describing* position *in two* dimensions.

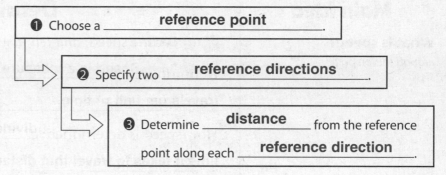

❶ Choose a ___reference point___ .

❷ Specify two ___reference directions___ .

❸ Determine ___distance___ from the reference point along each ___reference direction___ .

Describing Changes in Position

I found this on page ___13___ .

Define motion, *and explain how to determine whether* motion *has occurred.*

Motion is ___the process of changing position___ .

To tell whether an object is in motion, ___compare the object's position with that of a reference point. If the distance between the object and the reference point changes, motion has occurred___

I found this on page ___13___ .

🔑 **Differentiate** *distance and* displacement.

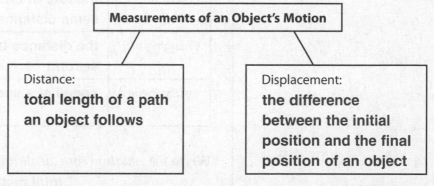

Measurements of an Object's Motion

Distance: **total length of a path an object follows**

Displacement: **the difference between the initial position and the final position of an object**

🔑 **Connect It** You are riding on a wagon. If you use the wagon as a reference point, are you moving? How do you know the wagon is moving?

Accept all reasonable responses. Sample answer: If the wagon is the reference point, you are not moving because your position relative to the wagon remains constant. You can tell that the wagon is in motion because the distance between the wagon and other objects in the environment changes.

Lesson 2 Speed and Velocity

> **Predict** *three facts that will be discussed in Lesson 2 after reading the headings. Write your facts in your Science Journal.*

■■■ Main Idea ■■■

What is speed?
I found this on page ___17___ .

I found this on page ___17___ .

I found this on page ___18___ .

I found this on page ___19___ .

I found this on page ___19___ .

■■■ Details ■■■

🔑 **Define** speed, *and tell how it is determined.*

Definition: **Speed is a measure of the distance an object travels per unit of time.**

How speed is determined: **divide distance traveled by the time it takes to travel that distance**

Determine *the* speed *of each event. Draw a line to the reasonable measurement of* speed *for that event.*

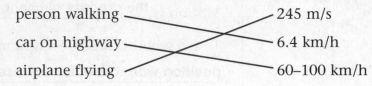

person walking ——————— 245 m/s
car on highway ——————— 6.4 km/h
airplane flying ——————— 60–100 km/h

Examine constant speed, *changing* speed, *and* instantaneous speed.

Speed	Description
Constant	the rate of change of position in which the same distance is traveled each second
Changing	the distance traveled is different each second
Instantaneous	speed at a specific instant in time

Write *the equation for calculating* average speed.

$$\text{average speed (in m/s)} = \frac{\text{total distance (in m)}}{\text{total time (in s)}} \quad \text{or} \quad v = \frac{d}{t}$$

Determine *the* speeds *in the following scenario.*

John drives 50 km/h for one hour and 100 km/h for one hour.

instantaneous speed each hour: **50 km/h for the first hour and 100 km/h for the second hour**

average speed for the two hours: **75 km/h**

Lesson 2 | Speed and Velocity (continued)

▪▪▪ **Main Idea** ▪▪▪ | ▪▪▪▪▪▪▪▪▪▪▪▪ **Details** ▪▪▪▪▪▪▪▪▪▪▪▪

Distance-Time Graphs

I found this on page ___20___.

Interpret *the distance-time graph to tell what happened in the race to the swing.*

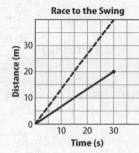
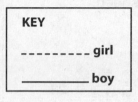

The boy and girl start from the school door. When the ___girl___ reaches the swing, the ___boy___ is 30 m from the school door.

I found this on page ___21___.

🔑 **Sequence** *the 5 steps used to calculate* average speed *of an object on a distance-time graph.*

1. __Choose one point on the line.__

2. __Choose a second point on the line.__

3. __Find the time difference of the points.__

4. __Find the distance difference of the points.__

5. __Divide difference in distance by difference in time.__

I found this on page ___21___.

🔑 **Calculate** *the* average speed *of the runner between seconds 4 and 6 using the five steps.*

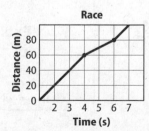

Allow students to use calculators to find the average speed.

Step 1. _4,60_

Step 2. _6,80_

Step 3. _Difference in time: 6s – 4 s = 2 s_

Step 4. _Difference in distance: 80 m – 60 m = 20 m_

Step 5. _Divide 20 by 2 = 10 m/s_

What is the runner's average speed? ___10 m/s___

Copyright © Glencoe/McGraw-Hill, a division of The McGraw-Hill Companies, Inc.

Lesson 2 | Speed and Velocity (continued)

■■■ Main Idea ■■■

I found this on page ___22___ .
Students can also list average speed.

I found this on page ___22___ .

■■■■■■■■■ Details ■■■■■■■■■

Identify *3 motions that can be shown on distance-time graphs.*

1. slowing down

2. stopping

3. speeding up

Calculate *the average speed of the marble.*

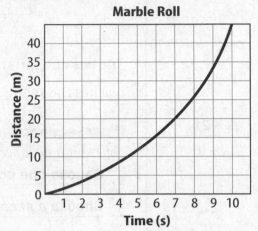

Marble Roll

Starting point: ___0,0___   Ending point: ___10,40___

Change in distance: ___40 m___   Change in time: ___10 s___

Average speed of the marble: ___40 m ÷ 10 s = 4 m/s___

Velocity

I found this on page ___23___ .

I found this on page ___23___ .

Define velocity.

velocity: ___the speed and direction of motion___

🔑 **Explain** *how* velocity *can change.*

Velocity changes when

- direction changes.
- speed changes.
- both speed and direction change.

🔑 **Analyze It** Explain how motion can be described using a distance-time graph.

Sample answer: A distance-time graph shows how the speed of an object changes

with time. A distance-time graph can also show when an object slows down, stops,

or speeds up.

> **Skim** *Lesson 3 in your book. Read the headings, and look at the photos and illustrations. Identify three things you want to learn more about as you read the lesson. Write your ideas in your Science Journal.*

■■■ **Main Idea** ■■■

Acceleration—Changes in Velocity

I found this on page _____27_____.

I found this on page _____28_____.

I found this on page _____28_____.

I found this on page _____28_____.

■■■■■■■■■■■■ **Details** ■■■■■■■■■■■■

Define acceleration.

acceleration: <u>a measure of the change in velocity during a</u>

<u>period of time</u>

🔑► **Identify** *3 ways that an object can accelerate.*

1. <u>slow down</u>

2. <u>speed up</u>

3. <u>change direction</u>

Describe *the acceleration of a car in each situation.*

	Description
Leaving an intersection	Acceleration increases in the same direction as that in which the car is moving.
Approaching an intersection	Acceleration increases in the opposite direction from that in which the car is moving.

Draw *arrows to show the direction of velocity and* acceleration *as the toy car moves along the track. Use one color to show velocity and another color to show* acceleration.

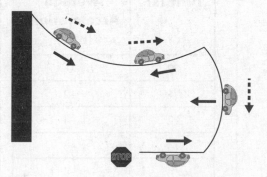

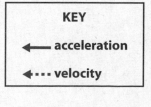

KEY

◄—— acceleration

◄···· velocity

▪▪▪ **Main Idea** ▪▪▪

Calculating Acceleration
I found this on page ____29____ .

I found this on page ____29____ .

I found this on page ____29____ .

I found this on page ____29____ .

▪▪▪▪▪▪▪▪▪ **Details** ▪▪▪▪▪▪▪▪▪

Define average acceleration, *and complete the equation for calculating it.*

average acceleration: **a change in velocity during a time interval divided by the time interval during which the velocity changes**

Average Acceleration Equation:

$$a = \frac{v_f - v_i}{t}$$

Identify *each variable in the equation.*

average acceleration: ___**a**___   final speed: ___**v_f**___

initial speed: ___**v_i**___   t: ___**time**___

Solve *for average acceleration.*

A rocket accelerates from 0 to 20 km/s. Five seconds after reaching 20 km/s, the rocket is traveling at 280 km/s. What is the average acceleration of the rocket?

initial speed: _____**20 km/s**_____

final speed: _____**280 km/s**_____

total time: _____**5 seconds**_____

$$a = \frac{280 \text{ km/s} - 20 \text{ km/s} = 260 \text{ km/s}}{5 \text{ s}}$$

What is the average acceleration of the rocket? ___**52 km/s**___

Determine *the direction of motion of two objects.*

Time (s)	Average Acceleration (m/s)	Time (s)	Average Acceleration (m/s)
0	0	0	0
1	−2	1	2
2	−4	2	4
3	−6	3	6
4	−8	4	8

Direction of motion: **negative**   Direction of motion: **positive**

■■■ **Main Idea** ■■■ | ■■■■■■■■■ **Details** ■■■■■■■■■■■

Speed-Time Graphs

I found this on page ___30___ .

🔑 **Explain** *what a speed-time graph indicates about an object's* motion.

how speed changes over time

I found this on page ___31___ .

🔑 **Describe** *the* motion *represented by each set of graphs.*

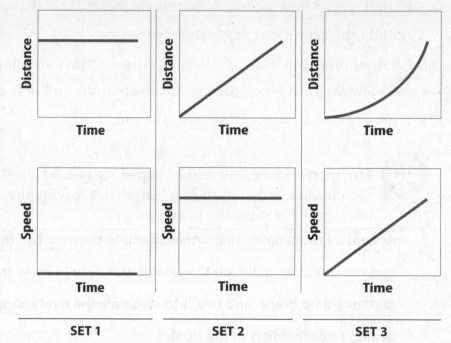

SET 1 | SET 2 | SET 3

SET 1. The object is at rest.

SET 2. The object is moving at a constant speed.

SET 3. The object is speeding up.

Summarizing Motion

I found this on page ___32___ .

Sample answers are shown.

Summarize *five ways* motion *can be described.*

1. _____position_____   4. _____velocity_____

2. _____average speed_____   5. _____acceleration_____

3. _____instantaneous speed_____

🔑 **Synthesize It** Draw a graph to show a car that starts from rest, accelerates to 35 km/h in 20 seconds, travels at a constant speed for 20 seconds, slows to a stop in 10 seconds, and remains at rest for 20 seconds. Label acceleration during each time period.

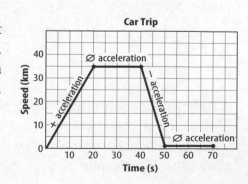

Describing Motion

Chapter Wrap-Up

Now that you have read the chapter, think about what you have learned.

Use this checklist to help you study.

❏ Complete your Foldables® Chapter Project.

❏ Study your *Science Notebook* on this chapter.

❏ Study the definitions of vocabulary words.

❏ Reread the chapter, and review the charts, graphs, and illustrations.

❏ Review the Understanding Key Concepts at the end of each lesson.

❏ Look over the Chapter Review at the end of the chapter.

THE BIG IDEA **Summarize It** Reread the chapter Big Idea and the lesson Key Concepts. Describe the position and motion of a boat that is leaving the dock. Explain how you could use a graph to show the boat's motion.

Accept all reasonable responses. Sample answer: The reference point is the dock,

and the direction in which the boat is traveling is away from the dock. I could make a

distance-time graph and use it to calculate the average speed or to calculate the

average acceleration of the boat.

_____

_____

_____

_____

_____

_____

_____

Challenge *Some things move so slowly or so quickly that motion is not visible. What events occur so slowly that you cannot see the motion happening? What events occur so quickly that you cannot see the motion happening? How could you determine that an object has moved, even when you cannot see the motion?*

The Laws of Motion

 How do forces change the motion of objects?

Before You Read

Before you read the chapter, think about what you know about forces and motion. Record your thoughts in the first column. Pair with a partner, and discuss his or her thoughts. Write those ideas in the second column. Then record what you both would like to share with the class in the third column.

Think	Pair	Share

Chapter Vocabulary

Lesson 1	Lesson 2	Lesson 3	Lesson 4
NEW force contact force noncontact force gravity mass weight friction **ACADEMIC** significant	**NEW** net force balanced forces unbalanced forces Newton's first law of motion inertia **REVIEW** reference direction	**NEW** Newton's second law of motion circular motion centripetal force	**NEW** Newton's third law of motion force pair momentum law of conservation of momentum

A Lesson Content Vocabulary page for each lesson is provided in the Chapter Resources Files.

Lesson 1 Gravity and Friction

> **Scan** *Lesson 1. Write three questions that you have about gravity and friction in your Science Journal. Try to answer your questions as you read.*

■■■ Main Idea ■■■

Types of Forces
I found this on page ___45___ .

I found this on page ___45___ .

I found this on page ___46___ .

I found this on page ___46___ .

Upward pointing arrow should be drawn distinguishably longer than downward pointing arrow.

■■■■■ Details ■■■■■

Model *forces on an object. Change the lines to arrows, and label them "push" or "pull."*

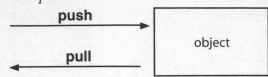

Contrast *types of forces, and give an example of each.*

Contact Forces	Noncontact Forces
Description: **a push or pull on one object by another that is touching it**	Description: **the force one object can apply to another without touching it**
Example: **Sample answer: an athlete hitting a ball with a bat**	Example: **Sample answer: a pencil falling to the floor**

Draw *arrows to represent the described forces.*

Description	Drawing
A slight downward force on the object	object
A greater upward force than the downward force illustrated above	object

Lesson 1 | Gravity and Friction (continued)

▪▪▪ **Main Idea** ▪▪▪ | ▪▪▪▪▪▪▪▪▪▪ **Details** ▪▪▪▪▪▪▪▪▪▪

What is gravity?

I found this on page _____47_____ .

Distinguish mass *and* gravity.

Mass	Gravity
the amount of matter in an object	the attractive force between all objects that have mass

I found this on page _____47_____ .

🔑 **Cite** *the law of universal gravitation.*

All objects are attracted to each other by a gravitational

force.

I found this on page _____47_____ .

Arrows for pairs that contain at least one larger mass should be distinguishably longer than arrows for pairs made up of two smaller masses. All arrow pairs should be the same size.

Illustrate *the relationship between gravitational* force *and* mass. *Draw arrows in the diagrams to indicate the size and direction of the attractive* force *of each object.*

Description	Diagram
Objects with smaller masses	
Objects with larger masses	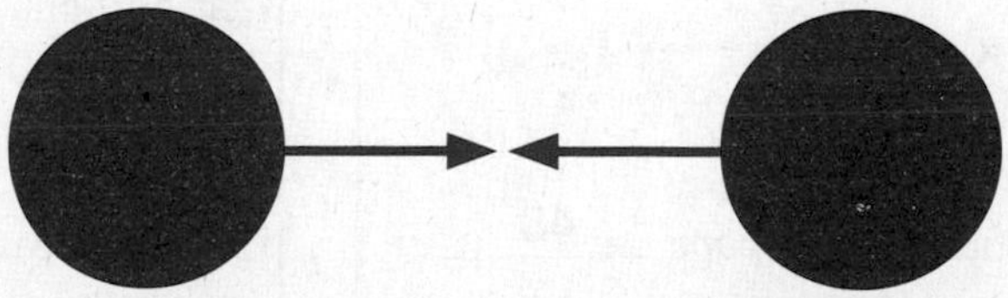
Objects with different masses	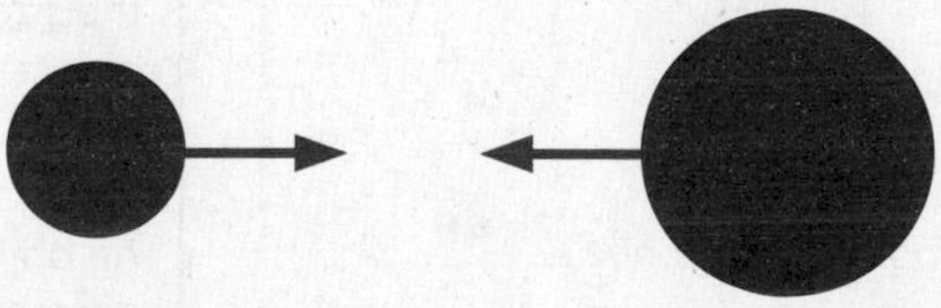

■■■ **Main Idea** ■■■ | ■■■■■■■■ **Details** ■■■■■■■■

I found this on page ___47___ .

Describe *the relationship between gravitational* force *and distance as shown in the diagram.*

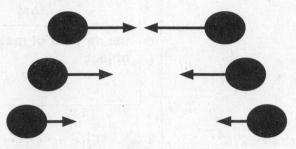

The gravitational force between the objects decreases as

distance between the objects increases.

_____

Assess *the information about* gravity, mass, *and* weight. *Read each statement. If it is true, write T in the center column. If it is false, write F in the center column and replace the underlined words to make the statement true.*

Statement	T or F	Corrected Statement
<u>Mass</u> is a gravitational force exerted <u>by</u> an object.	F	**Weight is a gravitational force exerted on an object.**
An object's <u>weight</u> is proportional to its <u>mass</u>.	T	
Mass is measured in <u>newtons</u>.	F	**Mass is measured in kilograms.**
If an object has twice the <u>size</u> of another object, it has <u>half</u> the weight.	F	**If an object has twice the mass of another object, it has twice the weight.**
An object's <u>mass</u> decreases the farther it gets from Earth's surface.	T	**An object's weight decreases the farther it gets from Earth's surface.**

I found this on page ___48___ .

I found this on page ___48___ .

I found this on page ___48___ .

I found this on page ___48___ .

I found this on page ___48___ .

Lesson 1 | Gravity and Friction (continued)

■■■ **Main Idea** ■■■ | ■■■■■■■■■ **Details** ■■■■■■■■

Friction

I found this on page ___49___ .

🔑 **Complete** *the concept map about* friction.

Friction
Definition: **a force that resists the motion of two surfaces that are touching**

I found this on page ___49___ .

static friction	sliding friction	**fluid friction**
prevents two surfaces from sliding past each other	**opposes motion of objects sliding past each other**	occurs between a surface and a material that flows

I found this on page ___50___ .

🔑 **Cite** *two reasons* friction *occurs between surfaces.*

1. **Microscopic dips and bumps on one surface catch on those of another surface when they slide past each other.**

2. **Attraction between electrical charges in surface particles slows their sliding past each other.**

I found this on page ___50___ .

Explain *how lubricants reduce* friction.
Lubricants decrease friction by slightly separating surfaces as they slide past each other.

🔑 **Connect It** Describe how the forces of gravity and friction affect the motion that occurs as you write on this page.

Accept all reasonable responses. Sample answer: Gravity pulls my Science Notebook to the surface of the desk. Friction keeps the book stationary on the desk unless I push the book with enough force to overcome static friction. Friction between my pencil and the page also determines how much force I must apply to the pencil to slide it along the page to write.

Predict *three facts that will be discussed in Lesson 2 after reading the headings. Record your predictions in your Science Journal.*

■■■ **Main Idea** ■■■

Identifying Forces

I found this on page ____55____.

I found this on page ____56____.

I found this on page ____56____.

I found this on page ____56____.

■■■■■■■■ **Details** ■■■■■■■■

Draw *the described forces. Use labeled arrows to indicate the forces on a box, and show the* net forces *in the column to the right.*

Description	Drawing	Net force
1. A force of 200 N to the left and another force of 50 N to the left **Drawings should show two left-pointing arrows on the right side of the box, one labeled 200 N and the other labeled 50 N.**		← 250 N
2. A force of 100 N to the right and a force of 80 N to the left **Drawings should show a right-pointing arrow on the left labeled 100 N and a left-pointing arrow on the right labeled 80 N.**		20 N →
3. A force of 180 N to the right and a force of 180 N to the left **Drawings should show a left-pointing arrow on the right and a right-pointing arrow on the left, both labeled 180 N.**		zero (0)

Identify *the forces in the table above as* balanced forces *or* unbalanced forces.

1. ____**unbalanced**____

2. ____**unbalanced**____

3. ____**balanced**____

■■■ Main Idea ■■■ | **■■■■■■■ Details ■■■■■■■■■**

Newton's First Law of Motion

I found this on page ____57____ .

🔑 **Summarize** Newton's first law of motion.

| If the net force on an object is zero, | an object at rest **will stay at rest** . |
| | an object in motion **will continue moving in a straight line with a constant speed** . |

I found this on page ____57____ .

🔑 **Contrast** *the motion of objects acted on by* balanced *and* unbalanced forces.

object's motion + ____**balanced**____ forces

= ____**unchanged**____ velocity

object's motion + ____**unbalanced**____ forces

= changed ____**velocity**____

I found this on page ____58____ .

🔑 **Explain** *the effect of* inertia *on objects at rest and objects in motion.*

Inertia is the tendency of an object to resist a change in its motion. It causes objects at rest to remain at rest and objects in motion to continue moving in a straight line at a constant speed unless outside forces intervene.

Why do objects stop moving?

I found this on page ____58____ .

🔑 **Summarize** *how* friction *and* inertia *act on an object sliding on a flat surface.*

Inertia causes the object to continue sliding, but friction slows the object's motion.

🔑 **Synthesize It** Look at the objects around you that are at rest. Explain why they are subjected to net forces of zero as opposed to no forces at all.

Accept all reasonable answers. Sample answer: All stationary objects on Earth are being acted on by gravity. In order for an object not to be set in motion by the gravitational force, a balanced force must bring the object to zero, allowing it to remain at rest.

Scan *Lesson 3. Read the lesson titles and bold words. Look at the pictures. Identify three facts that you discovered about Newton's second law of motion. Record your facts in your Science Journal.*

▪▪▪ **Main Idea** ▪▪▪

▪▪▪▪▪▪▪▪▪ **Details** ▪▪▪▪▪▪▪▪▪

How do forces change motion?
I found this on page __62__ .

Identify *2 characteristics of motion that can be changed by forces.*

1. _____ **speed** _____   2. _____ **direction** _____

I found this on page __63__ .

Cite *the effect of forces on an object at rest.*

Force		Effect
balanced	⇒	**The object will remain at rest.**

I found this on page __63__ .

| unbalanced | ⇒ | **The object will be set into motion.** |

Describe *the effect of forces on an object in motion.*

I found this on page __63__ .

Force		Effect
in the direction of the object's motion	⇒	**The object will speed up.**

I found this on page __63__ .

| in a direction other than that of the object's motion | ⇒ | **The object will slow down and/ or change direction.** |

I found this on page __64__ .

Recall *the difference between velocity and acceleration.*

Velocity	Acceleration
the speed and direction in which an object is moving	a change in velocity

Newton's Second Law of Motion
I found this on page __65__ .

🔑 **Summarize** Newton's second law of motion.

The _____ **acceleration** _____ of an object is equal to the

_____ **net force** _____ exerted on the object

_____ **divided by** _____ the object's _____ **mass** _____ .

▪▪▪ **Main Idea** ▪▪▪

I found this on page ___65___ .

Explain *the equation for* Newton's second law.

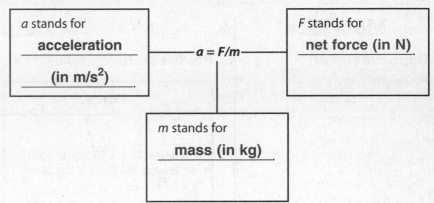

a stands for
__**acceleration**__
__**(in m/s²)**__

— *a = F/m* —

F stands for
__**net force (in N)**__

m stands for
__**mass (in kg)**__

Circular Motion

I found this on page ___66___ .

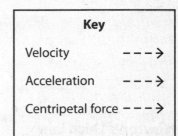 **Model** centripetal force *in a drawing of an object in circular motion. Use arrows of different colors to complete the key and to represent forces in the drawing.*

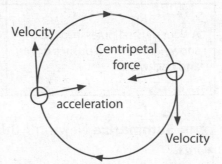

Key	
Velocity	- - - →
Acceleration	- - - →
Centripetal force	- - - →

Connect It When you begin pedaling a bike, you apply forces that set you and the bike in motion. Explain why you have to keep pedaling a bike to keep moving, and identify the forces that slow and stop you.

__Accept all reasonable responses. Sample answer: When I stop pedaling, inertia keeps the__

__bike in motion for a while, but then friction slows the bike. Soon the centripetal force of__

__gravity pulls the bike continually to one spot.__

_____

_____

_____

_____

Copyright © Glencoe/McGraw-Hill, a division of The McGraw-Hill Companies, Inc.

Scan *Lesson 4. Then write three questions that you have about Newton's third law of motion in your Science Journal. Try to answer your questions as you read.*

▪▪▪ **Main Idea** ▪▪▪ | ▪▪▪▪▪▪▪▪▪▪ **Details** ▪▪▪▪▪▪▪▪▪▪

Opposite Forces

I found this on page _____70_____ .

Predict *the corresponding result for each force.*

Force	Result
An airplane's jet engine pushes air toward the back of the plane.	**The air pushes back and the airplane moves forward.**
A fisherman tosses an anchor away from his boat.	**The anchor applies a force on the fisherman and his boat, pushing him in the opposite direction.**
A skier digs ski poles into the snowy ground and pushes down and backward.	**The ground pushes back and moves the skier forward.**

Newton's Third Law of Motion

I found this on page _____71_____ .

🔑 **Summarize** Newton's third law of motion *in your own words.*

Sample answer: When one object applies a force on a

second object, the second object applies a force of the

same size but in the opposite direction on the first object.

I found this on page _____71_____ .

Define force pair, *and identify the 2 parts of a* force pair.

```
Force pair: the forces two objects apply on
            each other
              │
      ┌───────┴───────┐
      │               │
  action force    reaction force
```

▪▪▪ **Main Idea** ▪▪▪ | ▬▬▬ **Details** ▬▬▬

I found this on page ___71___ .

Compare *forces in a* force pair.

Action force	Reaction force
Size	**equal size**
Direction	**opposite direction**

I found this on page ___71___ .

🔑 **Analyze** *why* force pairs *do not cancel each other.*

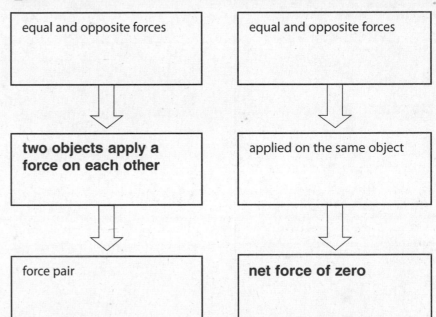

equal and opposite forces	equal and opposite forces
two objects apply a force on each other	applied on the same object
force pair	**net force of zero**

I found this on page ___71___ .

Summarize *the comparison above.*
Combining forces results in a net force of zero only if the

forces act on the same object.

I found this on page ___71___ .

Classify *forces in the sentences below. Underline action forces; circle reaction forces.*

A swimmer pushes his arms back against the water in a pool, and the water pushes forward against his arms.

A rocket engine pushes hot gas out in a downward direction, and the hot gas pushes upward on the engine.

A trampoline hurls a girl into the air.

●●● **Main Idea** ●●●●● | ●●●●●●●● **Details** ●●●●●●●●

Using Newton's Third Law of Motion
I found this on page ___72___ .

🔑 **Model** Newton's third law of motion *in a drawing. Label these terms:*

• action force   • force   • force pair

Drawings should represent an action force and a reaction force and should identify the two as a force pair. The directions of the forces in the pair should be opposite, and if the forces are not equal, the drawing should show motion.

Momentum
I found this on page ___73___ .

Define momentum.

the measure of how hard it is to stop a moving object

I found this on page ___73___ .

Explain *the equation for* momentum.

$$p = m \times v$$

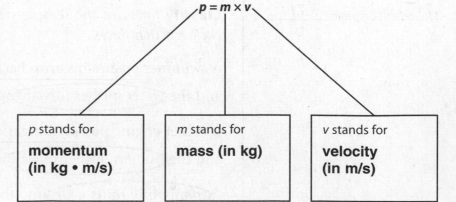

| *p* stands for **momentum (in kg • m/s)** | *m* stands for **mass (in kg)** | *v* stands for **velocity (in m/s)** |

Lesson 4 | Newton's Third Law (continued)

▪▪▪ **Main Idea** ▪▪▪ | ▪▪▪▪▪▪ **Details** ▪▪▪▪▪▪

I found this on page ___73___.

Analyze momentum. *Determine the* momentum *for each object. Circle the object that would be more difficult to stop.*

a 10-kg shopping cart moving at 5 m/s	(a 2-kg ball moving at 28 m/s)
10 kg x 5 m/s = 50 kg • m/s	2 kg x 28 m/s = 56 kg • m/s

Conservation of Momentum
I found this on page ___74___.

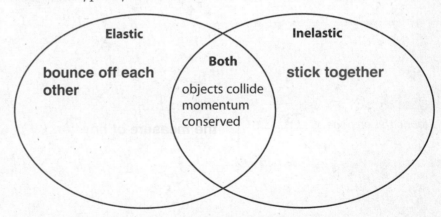 **Summarize** *the* law of conservation of momentum.

The _____total_____ momentum of a group of objects __stays the same unless outside forces__ act on the objects.

I found this on page ___74___.

Contrast *types of collisions.*

Elastic

bounce off each other

Both

objects collide momentum conserved

Inelastic

stick together

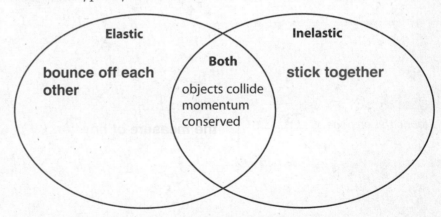 **Connect It** If you have ever been in a car at a stoplight beside a large truck, you probably noticed that the car took off from the stop much more quickly than the truck. Explain why it is harder to start and stop the motion of a large truck than that of a small car.

Accept all reasonable responses. Sample answer: The truck has a greater mass than the

car, so it requires more force to set it in motion. When the truck is moving, its greater

mass causes it to have greater momentum, making it harder to stop the motion.

The Laws of Motion

Chapter Wrap-Up

Now that you have read the chapter, think about what you have learned.

Use this checklist to help you study.

❑ Complete your Foldables® Chapter Project.

❑ Study your *Science Notebook* on this chapter.

❑ Study the definitions of vocabulary words.

❑ Reread the chapter, and review the charts, graphs, and illustrations.

❑ Review the Understanding Key Concepts at the end of each lesson.

❑ Look over the Chapter Review at the end of the chapter.

 Summarize It Reread the chapter Big Idea and the lesson Key Concepts. Draw a picture showing forces affecting objects in motion. Include at least six terms from the chapter as labels in your drawing, and explain the interaction of forces and motion.

Drawings should indicate forces causing and affecting motion of objects, including arrows showing sizes and directions of forces.

_____

Accept all reasonable responses. Sample answer: The swinging bat collides with

the ball. Conservation of momentum transfers most of the motion to the ball. The

net force against the ball is in the direction of the bat swing.

_____

_____

Challenge *Design simple demonstrations of Newton's laws of motion. Perform the demonstrations for your class, and explain them.*

Name _____ Date _____

Energy, Work, and Simple Machines

 How does energy cause change?

Before You Read

Before you read the chapter, think about what you know about energy and work. Record your ideas in the first column. Pair with a partner, and discuss his or her thoughts. Write those ideas in the second column. Then record what you both would like to share with the class in the third column.

Think	Pair	Share

Chapter Vocabulary

Lesson 1	Lesson 2	Lesson 3
NEW	**NEW**	**NEW**
energy	energy transformation	simple machine
kinetic energy	law of conservation of	inclined plane
electric energy	energy	screw
potential energy	work	wedge
chemical energy		lever
nuclear energy	**ACADEMIC**	wheel and axle
mechanical energy	transform	pulley
thermal energy		complex machine
sound energy		efficiency
seismic energy		
radiant energy		**REVIEW**
		plane

A Lesson Content Vocabulary page for each lesson is provided in the Chapter Resources Files.

Predict *three facts that will be discussed in Lesson 1 after reading the headings. Record your predictions in your Science Journal.*

■■■ **Main Idea** ■■■ | ■■■■■■■■■■■ **Details** ■■■■■■■■■■

What is energy?
I found this on page _____87_____ .

🔑 **Determine** *sources of energy for different objects.*

Car
gasoline or diesel

Your Body
food

Energy
Definition: **the ability to cause change**

Space Station
solar panels

Household Lights
electricity, changed from wind, coal, or another source

Kinetic Energy
I found this on page _____88_____ .

🔑 **Explain** *why electric energy is a type of kinetic energy.*
Accept all reasonable responses. Sample answer: The electrons that create electric current are moving. Kinetic energy is the energy an object has because it is in motion. Thus, electric energy is a type of kinetic energy.

Potential Energy
I found this on page _____89_____ .

Define *potential energy.*
Potential energy is stored energy that depends on the interaction of objects, particles, or atoms.

···Main Idea···

···Details···

🔑 **Describe** *types of* potential energy.

Type	Description
Gravitational potential energy	**potential energy stored in an object due to its height above Earth's surface**
Chemical energy	**energy stored in and released from the bonds between atoms**
Nuclear energy	**energy stored in and released from the nucleus of an atom**

I found this on page __89__ .

I found this on page __90__ .

Kinetic and Potential Energy Combined

I found this on page __91__ .

🔑 **Compare and contrast** mechanical energy *and* thermal energy. *Use the terms* kinetic energy *and* potential energy.

Mechanical Energy — **in a system of objects**

Both — **the sum of kinetic energy and potential energy**

Thermal Energy — **of the particles that make up an object**

I found this on page __91__ .

🔑 **Sequence** *the production of electricity from a geothermal* energy *source.*

Geothermal energy is used **to heat water and turn it into steam.**	Steam **turns turbines in electric generators.**	Electric generators **convert the kinetic energy into electricity.**

••• Main Idea ••• | ••••••••••• Details •••••••••••

Energy from Waves

I found this on page ___92___ .

 Describe *how waves are related to* sound energy, seismic energy, *and both.*

Sound Energy	Both	Seismic Energy
waves move through the air	carried by waves	waves move through the ground

I found this on page ___93___ .

 Characterize radiant energy.

Radiant Energy	carried by **electromagnetic waves**	through • **solids** • **liquids** • **gases** • **vacuum**

 Classify *uses of different types of* energy. *Review the lesson if you need help.*

Sample answers are shown.

I found this on page ___88___ .

I found this on page ___89___ .

I found this on page ___90___ .

I found this on page ___92___ .

I found this on page ___93___ .

Type	Example of Use
Kinetic	**converted by wind turbines into electricity**
Gravitational potential	**falling water used to produce electricity at a hydroelectric plant**
Chemical	**burning of fossil fuels used to power cars**
Sound	**a bat locating prey**
Radiant	**solar cells that provide energy to satellites**

 Connect It Identify three examples of energy you can observe from where you are right now.

Accept all reasonable responses. Sample answer: Radiant energy, sunlight, is

entering the window. My pencil has gravitational potential energy as I hold it in the air

above my desk. The lights are working because of electric energy.

Copyright © Glencoe/McGraw-Hill, a division of The McGraw-Hill Companies, Inc.

Lesson 2 Energy Transformations and Work

> **Scan** *Lesson 2. Read the lesson titles and bold words. Look at the pictures. Identify three facts you discovered about energy transformations. Record your facts in your Science Journal.*

▪▪▪ **Main Idea** ▪▪▪ | ▪▪▪▪▪▪▪▪▪▪▪ **Details** ▪▪▪▪▪▪▪▪▪▪▪

Energy Transformations
I found this on page __97__ .

Describe *an energy transfer and an* energy transformation.

A heat lamp warms a baby zebra.

Energy transfer:
Thermal energy transfers from the lamp to the air to the zebra.

Energy transformation:
The lamp converts electric energy to thermal energy.

Energy Conservation
I found this on page __97__ .

🔑 **Sequence** *a transformation of energy from the energy stored in the nuclei of atoms to radiant energy from a light bulb.*

| nuclear energy stored in atoms | **chemical energy in fuel at a power plant** | kinetic energy in a generator | **electrical energy in wiring** | radiant energy from a light bulb |

I found this on page __97__ .

🔑 **Paraphrase** *the* law of conservation of energy.
Energy cannot be created nor destroyed, but can only be

transformed from one form to another.

Lesson 2 | Energy Transformations and Work (continued)

■■■ Main Idea ■■■ | **■■■■■■■■■ Details ■■■■■■■■■**

I found this on page ___98___ .

Contrast *the energy present at different points of a roller coaster ride.*

At the top of the hill	Near the bottom of the hill
Gravitational potential energy: **high**	Gravitational potential energy: **low**
Kinetic energy: **low**	Kinetic energy: **high**

I found this on page ___98___ .

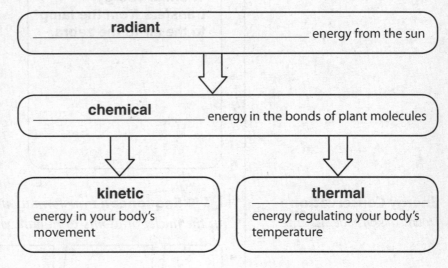

Order *an* energy transformation *that occurs through a plant to your body.*

_____ **radiant** _____ energy from the sun

⬇

_____ **chemical** _____ energy in the bonds of plant molecules

⬇   ⬇

kinetic   **thermal**

energy in your body's movement   energy regulating your body's temperature

Energy and Work

I found this on page ___99___ .

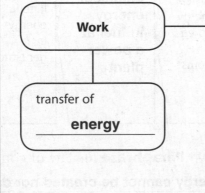

Characterize work.

Work

transfer of

energy

Related to a Force

• What makes the object move:

a force

• Direction of motion:

in the direction of the force

• When motion occurs:

while the force acts on the object

▪▪▪ **Main Idea** ▪▪▪ | ▪▪▪▪▪▪▪▪▪▪ **Details** ▪▪▪▪▪▪▪▪▪▪▪

I found this on page _____100_____ .

🔑 **Classify** *examples. Write* yes *if the example is* work, *and write* no *if the example is not. Explain your answers.*

Example	Yes or No	Explanation
You are lifting a ball off the ground.	**yes**	**The lifting force puts the ball in motion.**
You hold the ball.	**no**	**The ball is not in motion.**
You toss the ball into the air.	**no**	**No force is being applied after the ball is released.**
The ball falls toward the ground.	**yes**	**Gravity pulls the ball into downward motion.**

I found this on page _____100_____ .

Identify *the variables in the* work *equation.*

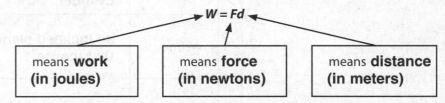

$$W = Fd$$

| means **work** (in joules) | means **force** (in newtons) | means **distance** (in meters) |

Energy and Heat
I found this on page _____101_____ .

Record *examples of waste energy during* energy transformations *and transfers in a race car.*

| Tires **heat from friction with the road** | Engine **heat from the engine that does not produce motion** | Air **heat from friction between air and the car** |

🔑 **Analyze It** Summarize the energy transformations, including waste energy, that take place when you ride a bicycle.

Accept all reasonable responses. Sample answer: Chemical energy from food I eat

converts to kinetic energy of my moving body. My body also gives off heat. I apply

force to the bike that makes it move. Some of the energy from that force transforms

to thermal energy from the friction of the bike tires against the street and the bike and

my body with the air.

Lesson 3 Machines

> **Skim** *Lesson 3 in your book. Read the headings and look at the photos and illustrations. Identify three things you want to learn more about as you read the lesson. Record your ideas in your Science Journal.*

■■■ Main Idea ■■■

Machines Transfer Mechanical Energy

I found this on page ____105____ .

I found this on page ____106____ .

I found this on page ____107____ .

I found this on page ____107____ .

Sample examples are shown.

■■■ Details ■■■

🔑 **Define** simple machines.

machines that do work using one movement

🔑 **Differentiate** simple machines.

Machine	Description	How It Makes Work Easier
Inclined plane	a flat, sloped surface	requires less force to move an object upward
Screw	an inclined plane wrapped around a cylinder	changes the direction of a force
Wedge	an inclined plane that moves	changes the direction of a force
Lever	a simple machine that pivots around a fixed point	decreases the input force required by increasing the distance
Wheel and axle	a shaft attached to a wheel of a larger diameter so both rotate together	increases output force
Pulley	a grooved wheel with a rope or cable wrapped around it	changes the direction of a force

Characterize complex machines.

Definition:
two or more simple machines working together

Example: a bicycle →

- pully: **turns the wheels**
- wheel and axle: **front wheel**
- lever: **pedals**

Lesson 3 | Machines (continued)

▪▪▪ **Main Idea** ▪▪▪ | ▪▪▪▪▪▪▪▪▪▪▪ **Details** ▪▪▪▪▪▪▪▪▪▪▪

Machines and Work
I found this on page ___108___ .

🔑 **Generalize** *ways in which machines make work easier.*
They change the direction or distance of force.

_____

Efficiency
I found this on page ___109___ .

Characterize efficiency.

Definition	Equation
the ratio of output work to input work	$\dfrac{W_{out}}{W_{in}}$ x 100%

Newton's Laws and Simple Machines
I found this on page ___110___ .

🔑 **Evaluate** *Newton's three laws of motion in relation to using a hammer to pull a nail.*

First law: Unless a force is applied on an object, its motion will remain unchanged.	**The force of a hammer used as a lever to pull out a nail changes the nail's motion.**
Second law: Acceleration equals force divided by mass.	You can calculate the acceleration of a hammer accelerating in the direction a hand is pulling it.
Third law: If one object applies a force on another object, the second object applies an equal and opposite force.	**The force of a nail pulls back equally against the force of the hammer.**

🔑 **Synthesize It** Summarize how work is made easier when you use a wheelbarrow to push a heavy load of gravel up a hill. Identify the machine that is not part of the wheelbarrow.

Accept all reasonable responses. Sample answer: The hill is a ramp, which is an

inclined plane. Rolling the load up the ramp is easier than lifting it straight up the

same height, but the distance is increased.

Energy, Work, and Simple Machines

Chapter Wrap-Up

Now that you have read the chapter, think about what you have learned.

Use this checklist to help you study.

- ❑ Complete your Foldables® Chapter Project.
- ❑ Study your *Science Notebook* on this chapter.
- ❑ Study the definitions of vocabulary words.
- ❑ Reread the chapter, and review the charts, graphs, and illustrations.
- ❑ Review the Understanding Key Concepts at the end of each lesson.
- ❑ Look over the Chapter Review at the end of the chapter.

THE BIG IDEA

Summarize It Reread the chapter Big Idea and the lesson Key Concepts. Draw and label a diagram of a machine being used to make work easier. Include captions that describe the forces, energy transfers, and energy transformations involved.

Accept all reasonable drawings. Student diagrams should show and describe the energy transfers/transformations that produce the input force, the function of the machine that changes the distance or direction of the force, and the kinetic energy (work) that results from the output force.

Challenge *Make an inventory list of all of the simple machines that you can find in your home and classroom. Share the list with your class, and invite your classmates to add their ideas.*

Name _____ Date _____

Sound and Light

 How do sound and light waves travel and interact with matter?

Before You Read

Before you read the chapter, think about what you know about sound and light. Record your thoughts in the first column. Pair with a partner, and discuss his or her thoughts. Write those thoughts in the second column. Then record what you both would like to share with the class in the third column.

Think	Pair	Share

Chapter Vocabulary

Lesson 1	Lesson 2	Lesson 3
NEW	**NEW**	**NEW**
sound wave	light source	mirror
pitch	light ray	lens
echo	transparent	cornea
	translucent	pupil
REVIEW	opaque	iris
longitudinal wave		retina
		ACADEMIC
		convert

A Lesson Content Vocabulary page for each lesson is provided in the Chapter Resources Files.

Scan *Lesson 1. Read the headings and bold words. Look at the pictures. Write three facts that you discovered about sound and how you hear. Record your facts in your Science Journal.*

▪▪▪ **Main Idea** ▪▪▪

What is sound?
I found this on page _____123_____ .

I found this on page _____124_____ .

▪▪▪▪▪▪▪▪ **Details** ▪▪▪▪▪▪▪▪

🔑 **Detail** *information about* sound waves.

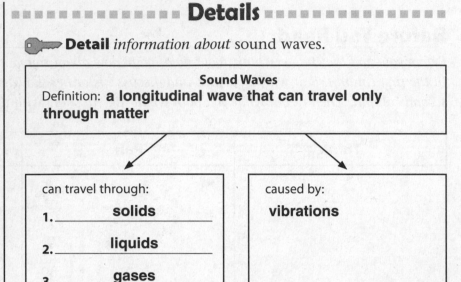

Sound Waves
Definition: **a longitudinal wave that can travel only through matter**

can travel through:

1. _____**solids**_____

2. _____**liquids**_____

3. _____**gases**_____

caused by:

vibrations

Model *a sound wave moving through air in the space below. Draw molecules as they would appear in compressions and rarefactions. Color the compressions red and rarefactions blue. Include these labels:*

- compression   • rarefaction   • wavelength

Drawings should include at least two compressions with a rarefaction between them. The molecules in the compressions should be close together. The molecules in the rarefactions should be spread apart. Rarefaction, compression, and wavelength should be labeled.

Lesson 1 | Sound (continued)

Main Idea

Speeds of Sound Waves
I found this on page _____125_____ .

Details

🔑 **Sequence** *the words solid, liquid, and gas on the continuum below, and then explain why these speed differences exist.*

sound travels slowest   sound travels fastest

⟵—————————————————————⟶

| gas | liquid | solid |

Explanation: Sample answer: A sound wave's speed is fastest when forces between particles in a material are stronger, and slower when forces are weaker. Solids usually have stronger forces; gases weaker forces.

I found this on page _____125_____ .

🔑 **Describe** *how temperature affects the speed of* sound waves.

As the temperature of a material increases, the speed of sound also increases.

The Human Ear
I found this on page _____126_____ .

Use a model of the human ear to reinforce the location and function of each part.

🔑 **Identify** *the parts of the human ear, and explain the function of each part.*

Part	Function
The outer ear	collects sound waves
The middle ear	amplifies sound waves as vibrations travel through three tiny bones called the hammer, the anvil, and the stirrup
The inner ear	converts vibrations to nerve signals that travel to the brain through the cochlea

∎∎∎ **Main Idea** ∎∎∎ | ∎∎∎∎∎∎∎∎∎∎∎ **Details** ∎∎∎∎∎∎∎∎∎∎

Sound and Pitch
I found this on page ___127___ .

Organize *information about* pitch.

Definition: **the perception of how high or low a sound seems**

Pitch —
organ in which humans produce sounds of different pitch: **vocal cords**

how humans change pitch: **by contracting or relaxing vocal cords**

I found this on page ___127___ .

Compare *the position of vocal cords when making sound.*

Event	Cause ⟶	Effect
Vocal cords tighten.	Muscles contract.	Pitch of voice is higher.
Vocal cords loosen.	Muscles relax.	Pitch of voice is lower.

Sound and Loudness
I found this on page ___128___ .

Draw *the compression and rarefaction of a low-amplitude* sound wave *and a high-amplitude* sound wave. *Color the compressions red and rarefactions blue. Include these labels:*

- compression
- rarefaction

Drawings should show the compression molecules close together. The rarefaction molecules should be scattered. Compression and rarefaction should be labeled.
Low Amplitude

Drawings should show the compression molecules more closely packed than in the low-amplitude sound. The rarefaction molecules should be more widely scattered than in the low-amplitude sound.
High Amplitude

Lesson 1 | Sound (continued)

<table>
<tr><td>■ ■ ■ **Main Idea** ■ ■ ■</td><td>■ ■ ■ ■ ■ ■ **Details** ■ ■ ■ ■ ■ ■</td></tr>
</table>

■■■ Main Idea ■■■

I found this on page **128** .

■■■■■ Details ■■■■■■

Analyze *information about decibel level and loudness.*

Amount of Energy	Decibels (dB)	Loudness
High	low / (high)	low / (high)
Low	(low) / high	(low) / high

Using Sound Waves
I found this on page **129** .

Allow students to use a large empty space, such as a gymnasium, to produce an echo.

Classify *types of reflected* sound waves *and their uses.*

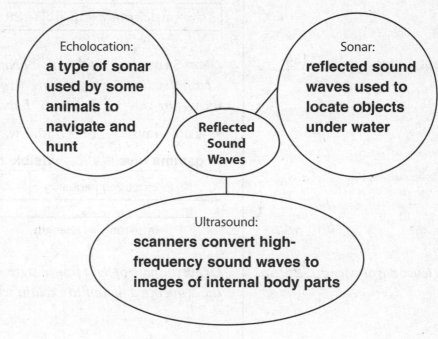

Echolocation:
a type of sonar used by some animals to navigate and hunt

Reflected Sound Waves

Sonar:
reflected sound waves used to locate objects under water

Ultrasound:
scanners convert high-frequency sound waves to images of internal body parts

🔑 **Connect It** Apply what you have learned about sound waves to describe the path of a sound wave from an electric guitar to the human ear.

Sample answer: Plucking or striking the guitar strings produces vibrations. These

vibrations are made louder by an amplifier. The vibrations travel through the air to the

ear. The outer ear collects the sound, the middle ear amplifies the vibrations, and the

inner ear converts the vibrations into nerve signals that the brain interprets as sound.

Lesson 2 Light

Predict *three facts that will be discussed in Lesson 2 after reading the headings. Record your facts in your Science Journal.*

▪▪▪ Main Idea ▪▪▪

What is light?
I found this on page ____133____.

I found this on page ____134____.

I found this on page ____135____.

▪▪▪▪▪▪ Details ▪▪▪▪▪▪

🗝️ **Compare** *light with sound waves. Read each description. Decide if it applies to light, to sound, or to both. Put a check mark in the appropriate column.*

Description	Light	Sound
Travels though matter	√	√
Travels though a vacuum	√	
Travels at different speeds in different materials	√	√

🗝️ **Sequence** *information about the electromagnetic spectrum. Color the line for increasing frequency purple and the line for increasing wavelength yellow. Label the diagram with these terms:*

- visible rays
- radio waves
- gamma rays

gamma rays	**visible rays**	**radio waves**

increasing frequency

increasing wavelength

Draw *the path of light from a light source to the eye. Then complete the sequence diagram to explain what you have drawn.*

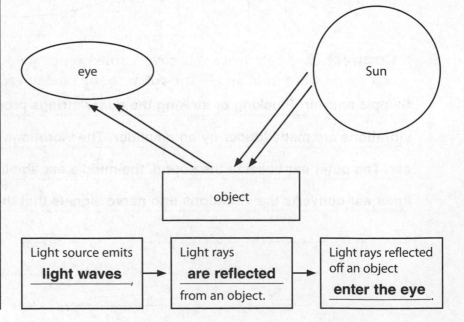

Light source emits **light waves**,	→	Light rays **are reflected** from an object.	→	Light rays reflected off an object **enter the eye**

▪▪▪ **Main Idea** ▪▪▪

The Interaction of Light and Matter

I found this on page _____136_____ .

Provide a variety of materials with different light-transmitting properties. Allow students to use a flashlight and experiment with each sample.

I found this on page _____136_____ .

▪▪▪ **Details** ▪▪▪

🔑 **Summarize** *each term below in your own words. Give three examples of a material with each light-transmitting property. Then circle how light interacts with matter to produce the effect.*

Material	Definition	Examples Sample answers shown.	How Light Interacts with Matter
Transparent	most light passes through; forms clear image	air, water, clear plastic bag	Reflected (Transmitted) (Absorbed)
Opaque	light does not pass through	milk, person, black construction paper	Reflected Transmitted (Absorbed)
Translucent	some light passes through; forms blurry image	shower curtain, ice cube, tracing paper	Reflected (Transmitted) (Absorbed)

Model *a light wave that reflects off a plane mirror at a 20° angle. Use a protractor to draw the angles on the mirror below. Include these labels:*

• angle of incidence   • angle of reflection   • normal

Color the angle of incidence red and the angle of reflection blue.

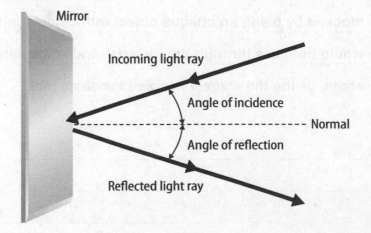

Mirror
Incoming light ray
Angle of incidence
Normal
Angle of reflection
Reflected light ray

Main Idea	**Details**
I found this on page ___137___ .	🔑 **Model** *scattering.* Draw what occurs when light rays encounter particles of dust floating in the air. Use these labels:

- air
- dust particles
- light rays

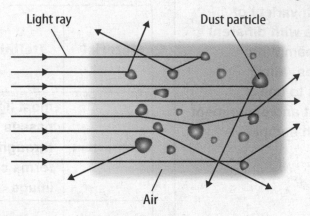

Light ray   Dust particle

Air

I found this on page ___137___ .

🔑 **Contrast** *reflection and refraction.*

Light Waves	
Reflection	**Refraction**
occurs when a light ray changes direction as it bounces off the surface of a material	occurs when a light ray bends as it changes speed

🔑 **Synthesize It** Suppose that you are designing the stage setting for a school play. Explain how you could give the stage a dappled sunshine appearance.

Accept all reasonable responses. Sample answer: A spotlight could be partially

blocked by using an opaque object with cutouts in the shape of leaves. Some light

would not pass through the material, and some light would strike the floor of the

stage, giving the stage a dappled sunshine look.

Lesson 3 **Mirrors, Lenses, and the Eye**

> **Skim** *Lesson 3 in your book. Read the headings and look at the photos and illustrations. Identify three things you want to learn more about as you read the lesson. Record your ideas in your Science Journal.*

▪▪▪ Main Idea ▪▪▪

Why are some surfaces mirrors?

I found this on page ___141___ .

Types of Mirrors

I found this on page ___142___ .

▪▪▪▪▪ Details ▪▪▪▪▪

🔑 **Draw** *the path of light rays in regular reflection and diffuse reflection.*

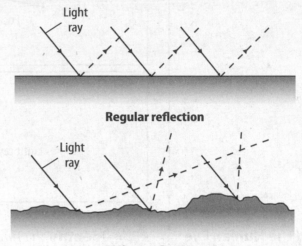

Regular reflection

Diffuse reflection

🔑 **Compare** *the 3 kinds of* mirrors *in the chart below.*

Mirror	Direction of Curvature	Direction of Reflected Light	Type of Image Rays Formed
Plane	flat	Light reflects at the same angle as the light rays hit the mirror.	reversed left to right
Concave	curved inward	When parallel light rays hit the mirror, they are reflected so that they pass through a focal point.	An object placed farther away than one focal length will appear upside down; an object placed closer than one focal length will appear right side up.
Convex	curved outward	Light rays spread apart as they are reflected.	always right side up and smaller than the original

▪▪▪ Main Idea ▪▪▪

▪▪▪ Details ▪▪▪

Types of Lenses

I found this on page _____143_____ .

🔑 **Contrast** *convex* lenses *and* concave *lenses. Draw how light rays travel through each type of* lens. *Label the focal point and focal length of the convex lens.*

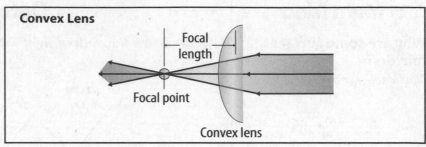

Convex Lens

Focal length

Focal point

Convex lens

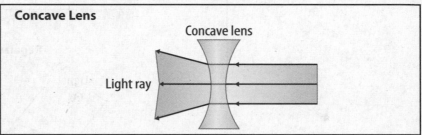

Concave Lens

Concave lens

Light ray

Light and the Human Eye

I found this on page _____144_____ .

Sample answers are shown.

Provide mirrors for students to watch their pupils expand and contract as the light levels are changed in the classroom.

🔑 **Identify** *the function of each part of the human eye.*

Lens: **made of flexible, transparent tissue that helps the eye form a sharp image of nearby and distant objects**

Iris: **colored part of the eye that controls the amount of light that enters the eye**

Cornea: **convex lens made of transparent tissue located on the outside of the eye**

Pupil: **the dark opening in the interior of the eye through which light enters**

Retina: **a layer of special light-sensitive cells in the back of the eye**

contains 2 light-sensitive cells:

a. rod cells: **sensitive to low-light; enable you to see in dim light**

b. cone cells: **three types of cone cells that enable you to see color**

Lesson 3 | Mirrors, Lenses, and the Eye (continued)

▪▪▪ Main Idea ▪▪▪ | ▪▪▪▪▪▪▪▪▪▪▪ Details ▪▪▪▪▪▪▪▪▪▪▪

The Colors of Objects

I found this on page ___147___ .

Distinguish *the color reflected from the colors absorbed by each block. Part of the table has been completed for you.*

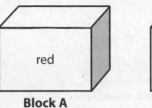 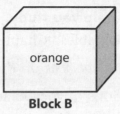 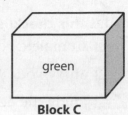

| Block A | Block B | Block C |

Colors(s)	Block A	Block B	Block C
Reflected	red	orange	green
Absorbed	orange, yellow, green, blue, indigo, violet	red, yellow, green, blue, indigo, violet	red, orange, yellow, blue, indigo, violet

I found this on page ___148___ .

Use a prism to show that when white light is bent, the different wavelengths spread out.

Evaluate *how a prism separates white light.*

Different ___wavelengths___ of light are ___bent___ by different amounts as they ___enter___ the prism and again when they ___exit___ the prism.

I found this on page ___148___ .

Identify *the color that the blue block will appear under different colored lights. Color each block the color you would see under each light.*

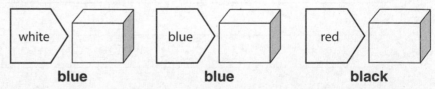

white ▸ **blue**   blue ▸ **blue**   red ▸ **black**

🔑 **Connect It** Describe how a rainbow would look if viewed through an indigo filter. Explain why the rainbow would appear this way.

Accept all reasonable responses. Sample answer: The colors red, orange, yellow, and

green would appear dark or black. Blue and indigo would be seen as blue and indigo.

Violet would be seen as black.

Sound and Light

Chapter Wrap-Up

Now that you have read the chapter, think about what you have learned.

Use this checklist to help you study.

❏ Complete your Foldables® Chapter Project.

❏ Study your *Science Notebook* on this chapter.

❏ Study the definitions of vocabulary words.

❏ Reread the chapter, and review the charts, graphs, and illustrations.

❏ Review the Understanding Key Concepts at the end of each lesson.

❏ Look over the Chapter Review at the end of the chapter.

THE BIG IDEA **Summarize It** Reread the chapter Big Idea and the lesson Key Concepts. Use what you know to describe how sound and light interact with matter.

Accept all reasonable responses. Sample answer: Sound waves travel through solids, liquids, and gases at different speeds. Temperature also affects the speed of sound waves. Ears enable people to hear and transport vibrations to the brain, which interprets the vibrations. Humans can produce sound and can change the pitch and volume of their sounds. When light waves interact with matter, they can be transmitted, absorbed, or reflected. Light enables people to see. Light is focused in the eye, and the brain interprets the image. The light reflected from an object determines its color.

Challenge *Suppose that you are designing a musical instrument. Describe the instrument, explaining how it will make sound, and tell how you can change the pitch of the instrument's sound.*

Thermal Energy

 How can thermal energy be used?

Before You Read

Before you read the chapter, think about what you know about thermal energy. Record your ideas in the first column. Pair with a partner, and discuss his or her thoughts. Write those ideas in the second column. Then record what you both would like to share with the class in the third column.

Think	Pair	Share

Chapter Vocabulary

Lesson 1	Lesson 2	Lesson 3
NEW	**NEW**	**NEW**
thermal energy	radiation	heating appliance
temperature	conduction	thermostat
heat	thermal conductor	refrigerator
	thermal insulator	heat engine
REVIEW	specific heat	
kinetic energy	thermal expansion	
potential energy	thermal contraction	
	convection	
	convection current	

A Lesson Content Vocabulary page for each lesson is provided in the Chapter Resources Files.

Thermal Energy, Temperature, and Heat

> **Predict** *three facts that will be discussed in Lesson 1 after reading the headings. Record your predictions in your Science Journal.*

■■■ **Main Idea** ■■■

■■■■■■■■■■ **Details** ■■■■■■■■■■

Kinetic and Potential Energy

I found this on page ____165____ .

Relate *descriptions of energy.*

	Kinetic Energy	**Potential Energy**
Mechanical energy	the energy an object or particle has because it is moving	stored energy (due to the interaction between two objects)

What is Thermal Energy?

I found this on page ____166____ .

Characterize thermal energy, *and explain why matter has it.*

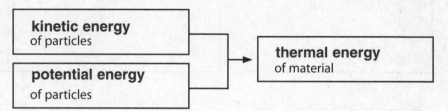

Explanation: **All particles within matter are in motion (kinetic energy), and they interact with one another (potential energy).**

What is temperature?

I found this on page ____167____ .

🔑 **Explain** *how kinetic energy of the particles relates to differences in* temperature *represented by the pictures.*

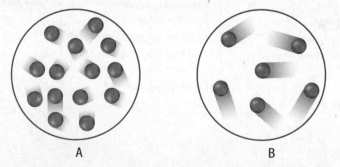

A   B

The particles in B are moving faster than the particles in A.

Because the particles in B are moving faster, they have

more kinetic energy. The higher average kinetic energy

means B represents a higher temperature.

▪▪▪ **Main Idea** ▪▪▪ | ▪▪▪▪▪▪▪▪▪▪▪▪▪▪▪▪▪ **Details** ▪▪▪▪▪▪▪▪▪▪▪▪▪▪

I found this on page ___167___ .

🔑 **Assess** *the* *difference* *between* thermal energy *and* temperature.

Thermal energy is the sum of kinetic and potential energy

of particles in a material; temperature is a measure of the

average kinetic energy only.

I found this on page ___168___ .

Contrast *common* temperature *scales.*

Scale	Water Freezes	Water Boils
Celsius	0°C	100°C
Kelvin	273 K	373 K
Fahrenheit	32°F	212°F

What is heat?
I found this on page ___169___ .

🔑 **Evaluate** *the difference between* heat *and* thermal energy.

All objects have thermal energy, but the energy must

transfer from one object to another to be considered heat.

I found this on page ___169___ .

🔑 **Relate** temperature *of objects to rate of* heat *transfer.*

Temperature Difference Between Objects	Rate Heating Occurs
greater	**faster**
lesser	**slower**

🔑 **Analyze It** Describe a hot summer day using the vocabulary terms and Key Concepts from this lesson.

Accept all reasonable responses. Sample answer: The temperature of the air is high,

which means that the air has greater average kinetic energy than air does when it

feels cooler outside. The temperature rises in the house as the day goes on and the

warmer outside air heats (transfers thermal energy to) the cooler air in the house.

Scan *Lesson 2. Read the lesson titles and bold words. Look at the pictures. Identify three facts you discovered about thermal energy transfers. Record your facts in your Science Journal.*

■■■ **Main Idea** ■■■

■■■■■■■■■■■■■■■ **Details** ■■■■■■■■■■■

How is thermal energy transferred?
I found this on page ____173____ .

Identify *3 ways thermal energy is transferred.*

1. radiation

2. conduction

3. convection

Radiation
I found this on page ____173____ .

Characterize radiation.

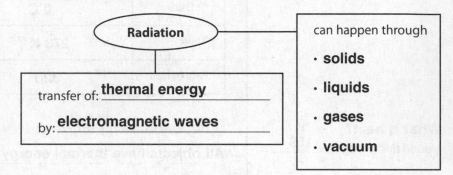

Radiation

transfer of: **thermal energy**
by: **electromagnetic waves**

can happen through

· **solids**

· **liquids**

· **gases**

· **vacuum**

Conduction
I found this on page ____174____ .

Describe conduction.

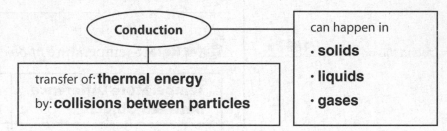

Conduction

transfer of: **thermal energy**
by: **collisions between particles**

can happen in

· **solids**

· **liquids**

· **gases**

I found this on page ____174____ .

Contrast *the* conduction *and* specific heat *of* thermal conductors *and* thermal insulators.

	Thermal Conductor	Thermal Insulator
Ease of conduction	easy	not easy
Relative specific heat	lower	higher
Reason	electrons move easily	electrons do not move as easily

▪▪▪ Main Idea ▪▪▪ | ▪▪▪▪▪▪▪▪▪▪▪▪▪▪ Details ▪▪▪▪▪▪▪▪▪▪▪▪▪

Thermal Expansion and Contraction

🔑 **Classify** *characteristics of* thermal expansion *and* thermal contraction.

I found this on page ___176___ .

I found this on page ___177___ .

Thermal Expansion	Thermal Contraction
Definition: **an increase in a material's volume when the temperature is increased**	Definition: **a decrease in a material's volume when the temperature is decreased**
Effect in a hot air balloon: **The air inside the balloon heats and expands. Some of the air is pushed out of the balloon, making it less dense than the surrounding air, and the balloon rises.**	Effect in a hot air balloon: **The air inside the balloon cools and contracts; air from outside the balloon rushes in to fill the space, the balloon's density increases, and the balloon descends.**

Convection

I found this on page ___178___ .

🔑 **Characterize** convection.

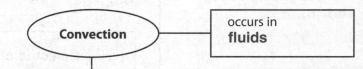

Convection — occurs in **fluids**

transfer of: **thermal energy**

by: **movement of particles from one part of a material to another**

I found this on page ___179___ .

Explain *atmospheric* convection currents.

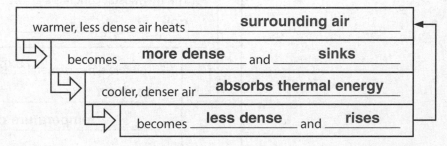

warmer, less dense air heats ___surrounding air___

becomes ___more dense___ and ___sinks___

cooler, denser air ___absorbs thermal energy___

becomes ___less dense___ and ___rises___

🔑 **Analyze It** Explain how all three processes that transfer thermal energy occur as you heat soup on a stove.

Accept all reasonable responses. Sample answer: The burner heats the pan through

conduction; convection currents transfer thermal energy throughout the fluid of the

soup; and I can feel the heat through radiation when I place my hand near the pan.

Skim *Lesson 3 in your book. Read the headings and look at the photos and illustrations. Identify three things you want to learn more about as you read the lesson. Record your ideas in your Science Journal.*

■■■ **Main Idea** ■■■ | ■■■ **Details** ■■■

Thermal Energy Transformations
I found this on page ___183___ .

Complete *the concept of thermal energy transformation.*

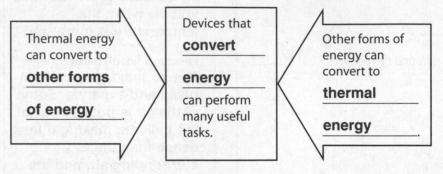

Thermal energy can convert to **other forms** **of energy**

Devices that **convert** **energy** can perform many useful tasks.

Other forms of energy can convert to **thermal** **energy**

Heating Appliances
I found this on page ___183___ .

Sample examples are shown.

Characterize heating appliances.

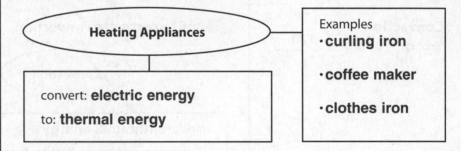

Heating Appliances

convert: **electric energy**
to: **thermal energy**

Examples
· **curling iron**
· **coffee maker**
· **clothes iron**

Thermostats
I found this on page ___184___ .

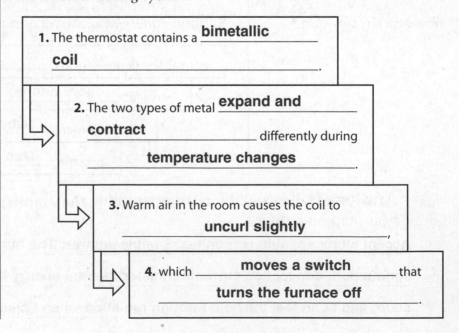

Sequence *concepts and steps in the function of a thermostat in a home heating system.*

1. The thermostat contains a **bimetallic** **coil**

2. The two types of metal **expand and** **contract** differently during **temperature changes**

3. Warm air in the room causes the coil to **uncurl slightly**,

4. which **moves a switch** that **turns the furnace off**

▪▪▪ **Main Idea** ▪▪▪

▪▪▪▪▪▪▪▪▪▪▪▪▪ **Details** ▪▪▪▪▪▪▪▪▪▪▪▪▪

Refrigerators

I found this on page ___185___ .

🗝 **Describe** *the transfers of thermal energy that occur in the function of a* refrigerator.

Step in the Process	Effect on Thermal Energy
Mechanical energy in the compressor compresses the coolant.	**Compression increases the thermal energy of the coolant.**
Thermal energy of the coolant is greater than the surrounding air.	**Thermal energy moves from the coolant to the air.**
Coolant becomes a liquid.	**Coolant loses thermal energy.**
Expander changes coolant from liquid to gas.	**Gas has less thermal energy, becomes colder.**
Cold gas passes through pipes in the refrigerator compartment.	**Coolant gas absorbs thermal energy from the refrigerator interior.**
The gas becomes warmer.	**The food becomes cooler.**

Warmed gas passes through compressor.

Heat Engines

I found this on page ___186___ .

🗝 **Order** *the energy conversions in the* heat engine *of a car.*

Chemical energy from fuel

converts to **thermal** _____

energy _____ during combustion.

About ___20___% converted to

mechanical _____

energy _____

🗝 **Synthesize It** Identify one device in or near your home that converts chemical energy to thermal energy, one device that converts electric energy to thermal energy, and one device that converts thermal energy to mechanical energy.

Accept all reasonable responses. Sample answer: The toaster converts electric

energy to thermal energy. The gas stove converts chemical energy to thermal energy.

The refrigerator thermostat converts thermal energy to mechanical energy.

Chapter Wrap-Up

Now that you have read the chapter, think about what you have learned.

Use this checklist to help you study.

❏ Complete your Foldables® Chapter Project.

❏ Study your *Science Notebook* on this chapter.

❏ Study the definitions of vocabulary words.

❏ Reread the chapter, and review the charts, graphs, and illustrations.

❏ Review the Understanding Key Concepts at the end of each lesson.

❏ Look over the Chapter Review at the end of the chapter.

 Summarize It Reread the chapter Big Idea and the lesson Key Concepts. Model what you have learned by drawing and labeling a diagram of a device that works because of its transfer and conversion of thermal energy.

Accept all reasonable responses. Student drawing should represent a device that functions based on the behavior of thermal energy between materials. Labels should indicate whether the transfer of energy occurs by radiation, conduction, or convection; they should describe the conversion of thermal energy into or from other forms of energy.

Challenge *Do an inventory of all of the useful devices in your home. Make a large chart that shows the thermal energy conversions that occur during the use of each device. Hint: Be sure not to overlook very simple devices. When you rub a pencil on paper to write a line, does a change in kinetic or thermal energy occur?*

States of Matter

 What physical changes and energy changes occur as matter goes from one state to another?

Before You Read

Before you read the chapter, think about what you know about states of matter. Record three things that you already know about matter in the first column. Then write three things that you would like to learn about changes in matter in the second column. Complete the final column of the chart when you have finished this chapter.

K What I Know	W What I Want to Learn	L What I Learned

Chapter Vocabulary

Lesson 1	Lesson 2	Lesson 3
NEW solid liquid viscosity surface tension gas vapor **REVIEW** matter	**NEW** kinetic energy temperature thermal energy vaporization evaporation condensation sublimation deposition	**NEW** kinetic molecular theory pressure Boyle's Law Charles's Law **ACADEMIC** theory

A Lesson Content Vocabulary page for each lesson is provided in the Chapter Resources Files.

Scan *Lesson 1. Read the lesson titles and bold words. Look at the pictures. Identify three facts you discovered about matter. Record your facts in your Science Journal.*

■■■ **Main Idea** ■■■

Describing Matter
I found this on page ___199___ .

I found this on page ___199___ .

■■■■■■■■■ **Details** ■■■■■■■■■

Recall *the states of matter.*

1. _____solid_____   3. _____liquid_____

2. _____gas_____   4. _____plasma_____

Characterize *ways to describe matter.*

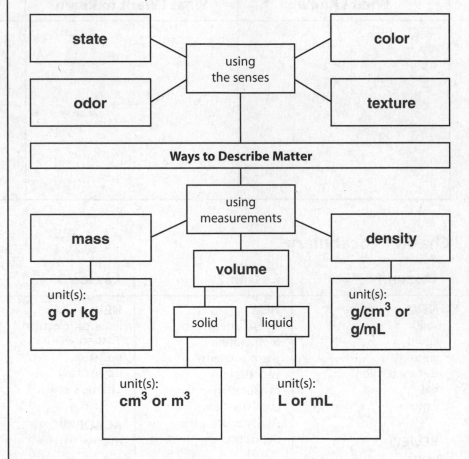

I found this on page ___200___ .

I found this on page ___200___ .

Identify *two factors that determine the state of matter.*

1. ___particle motion___   2. ___particle forces___

Explain *the free motion of particles.*

If particles are free to move, they move in a straight line

until they collide with something.

Lesson 1 | Solids, Liquids, and Gases (continued)

Main Idea

I found this on page ___200___ .

Details

Relate *particle motion to the distance between particles.*

Particle Speed	slow	faster	fastest
Strength of attractive forces	**strong**	**weaker**	**very weak**
Space between particles	tight	increased	spread out
Particle motion	**vibrate in place**	**slide past one another**	**move randomly**

Solids

I found this on page ___201___ .

🔑 **Characterize** solids.

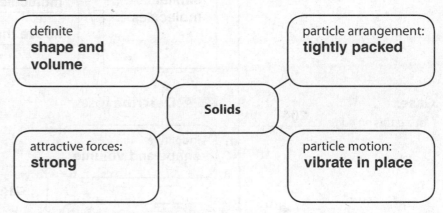

- definite **shape and volume**
- particle arrangement: **tightly packed**
- **Solids**
- attractive forces: **strong**
- particle motion: **vibrate in place**

I found this on page ___201___ .

Differentiate *crystalline* solids *from amorphous* solids.

Crystalline Solids	Amorphous Solids
Particle arrangement: **specific repeating order**	Particle arrangement: **random**
Example property: **very hard material**	Example property: **brittle**

▪▪▪ **Main Idea** ▪▪▪ | ▪▪▪▪▪▪▪▪▪▪ **Details** ▪▪▪▪▪▪▪▪▪▪

Liquids
I found this on page ___202___ .

⚷ Characterize liquids.

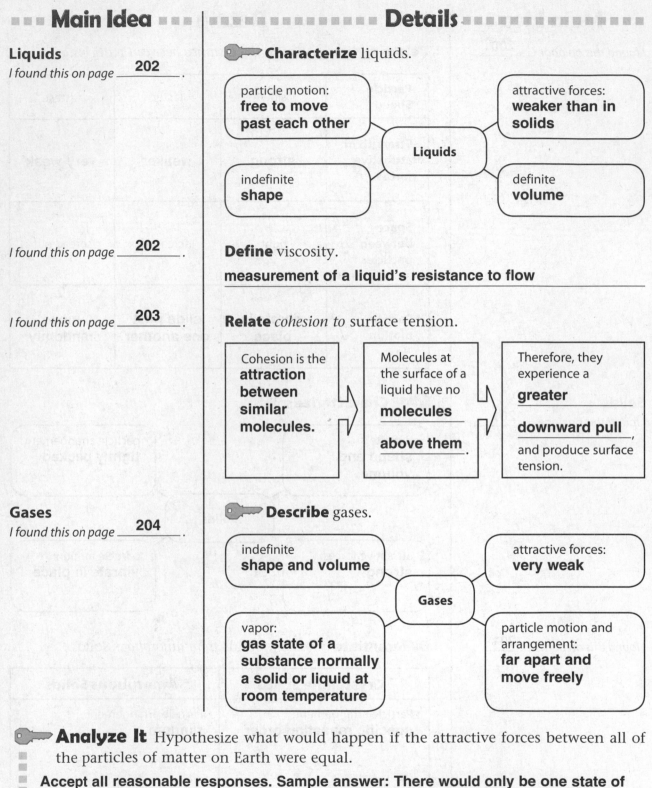

particle motion: **free to move past each other**

attractive forces: **weaker than in solids**

Liquids

indefinite **shape**

definite **volume**

I found this on page ___202___ .

Define viscosity.

measurement of a liquid's resistance to flow

I found this on page ___203___ .

Relate *cohesion to* surface tension.

Cohesion is the **attraction between similar molecules.** ⇒ Molecules at the surface of a liquid have no **molecules above them** . ⇒ Therefore, they experience a **greater** **downward pull**, and produce surface tension.

Gases
I found this on page ___204___ .

⚷ Describe gases.

indefinite **shape and volume**

attractive forces: **very weak**

Gases

vapor: **gas state of a substance normally a solid or liquid at room temperature**

particle motion and arrangement: **far apart and move freely**

⚷ Analyze It Hypothesize what would happen if the attractive forces between all of the particles of matter on Earth were equal.

Accept all reasonable responses. Sample answer: There would only be one state of

matter at any given time. If all particles of matter had strong attractive forces,

everything would be solid; if all particles had weaker attractive forces, everything

might be liquid or gas.

Predict *three facts that will be discussed in Lesson 2 after reading the headings. Write your facts in your Science Journal.*

▪▪▪ **Main Idea** ▪▪▪

▪▪▪▪▪▪▪▪▪▪▪▪▪ **Details** ▪▪▪▪▪▪▪▪▪▪▪▪▪

Kinetic and Potential Energy

I found this on page ___208___.

🔑 **Relate** kinetic energy *and* temperature *to particle motion.* *Draw arrows to show correlating increase or decrease.*

Particle Motion	Kinetic Energy of Particles	Temperature
⬆	⇧	⇧

I found this on page ___209___.

Contrast *the potential energy of particles.*

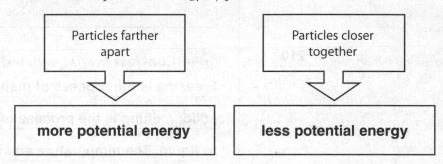

Particles farther apart → **more potential energy**

Particles closer together → **less potential energy**

Thermal Energy
I found this on page ___209___.

Detail *changes in* thermal energy.

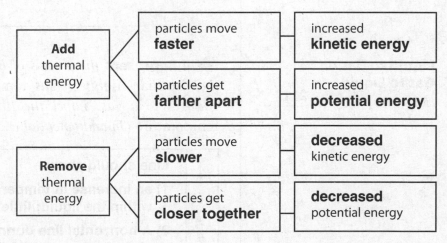

Add thermal energy	particles move **faster**	increased **kinetic energy**
	particles get **farther apart**	increased **potential energy**
Remove thermal energy	particles move **slower**	decreased kinetic energy
	particles get **closer together**	decreased potential energy

I found this on page ___209___.

🔑 **Compare** thermal energy *with* temperature.

Thermal energy is the total kinetic and potential energy of

an object; temperature is the average of the kinetic energy

only.

■■■ Main Idea ■■■   ■■■■■■■■■■■■ Details ■■■■■■■■■■■■■

Solid to Liquid or Liquid to Solid

I found this on page _____210_____.

Model *the process of melting. Draw a line to indicate the* thermal energy *versus* temperature *changes as a solid changes to a liquid. Label the line to indicate the changes in* temperature *(T) and potential energy (PE).*

> *Temperature Increases ↑*
>
> **Line should show**
>
> 1) an increase in temperature and thermal energy within the solid; little change in PE.
>
> 2) a horizontal line during which the solid changes to a liquid. T is constant; PE increases.
>
> 3) an increase in temperature and thermal energy to the now liquid matter; PE has little change.
>
> Thermal Energy Increases →

I found this on page _____210_____.

Contrast *freezing with melting.*

Freezing is the process of matter changing from liquid to solid; melting is the process of matter changing from solid to liquid. The temperature and thermal energy changes that occur during freezing are opposite those during melting.

Liquid to Gas or Gas to Liquid

I found this on page _____211_____.

Represent *the process of boiling. Draw a line to indicate the* thermal energy *versus* temperature *changes as a liquid changes to a gas. Label the line to indicate the changes in* temperature *(T) and potential energy (PE).*

> *Temperature Increases ↑*
>
> **Line should show**
>
> 1) an increase in temperature and thermal energy within the liquid; little change in PE.
>
> 2) A horizontal line during which the liquid changes to a gas (boiling). T is constant; PE increases.
>
> 3) an increase in temperature and thermal energy to the now gaseous matter; PE has little change.
>
> Thermal Energy Increases →

Copyright © Glencoe/McGraw-Hill, a division of The McGraw-Hill Companies, Inc.

▪▪▪ **Main Idea** ▪▪▪ | ▪▪▪▪▪▪▪▪▪▪▪▪▪ **Details** ▪▪▪▪▪▪▪▪▪▪▪▪

I found this on page ____211____ .

Differentiate *terms associated with changes of state.*

Term	Description
Vaporization	**change in state of a liquid into a gas**
Evaporation	**vaporization that occurs on the surface of a liquid**
Boiling	**vaporization that occurs within a liquid**
Condensation	**change in state of a gas into a liquid**

Solid to Gas or Gas to Solid

I found this on page ____212____ .

Compare *sublimation with deposition.*

Both are changes between solid and gaseous states

without passing through the liquid state.

States of Water

I found this on page ____213____ .

Characterize *water.*

Melting point: ____**0° C**____ Boiling point: ____**100° C**____

Unique because: **It exists as a solid, liquid, and gas within**

Earth's temperature range.

Conservation of Mass and Energy

I found this on page ____214____ .

Restate *concepts of conservation of mass and energy.*

Mass: Matter changes ____**state**____, but the total amount

of the matter ____**remains the same**____ .

Energy: Thermal energy is sometimes ____**absorbed**____ by

surrounding matter, but the total energy is ____**conserved**____ .

🔑 **Connect It** Suppose that you want to compare the mass of a block of ice to its mass as liquid water. You mass the ice, and then you mass a pan. You put the ice in the pan and place it over high heat. What will you find if you measure the mass of the water after it has been boiling for several minutes?

Accept all reasonable responses. Sample answer: After the water has been boiling for

a while, its mass will be less than the mass of the ice. Some of the water will have left

the pan as water vapor.

Skim *Lesson 3 in your book. Read the headings and look at the photos and illustrations. Identify three things you want to learn more about as you read the lesson. Record your ideas in your Science Journal.*

■■■ **Main Idea** ■■■

Understanding Gas Behavior
I found this on page _____218_____ .

What is pressure?
I found this on page _____219_____ .

Pressure and Volume
I found this on page _____219_____ .

Boyle's Law
I found this on page _____220_____ .

■■■ **Details** ■■■

🔑 **Paraphrase** *the basic ideas in* kinetic molecular theory.

1. Small particles make up all matter.

2. Particles are in constant, random motion.

3. Particles collide with other particles, other objects, and the walls of their container.

4. When particles collide, no energy is lost.

Describe pressure.
the amount of force applied per unit of area

Relate *volume to* pressure *of a gas at a constant temperature.*

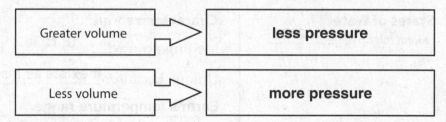

| Greater volume | ➤ | **less pressure** |
| Less volume | ➤ | **more pressure** |

Explain *the principle represented by the graph if the gas is at a constant temperature.*

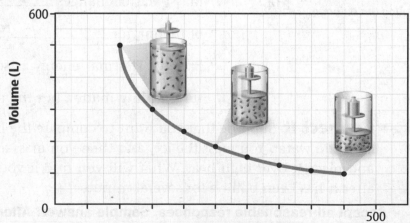

Boyle's Law—As volume increases, pressure decreases; as volume decreases, pressure increases.

Lesson 3 | The Behavior of Gases (continued)

<table>
<tr><td colspan="2">■ ■ ■ Main Idea ■ ■ ■</td><td>■ ■ ■ ■ ■ ■ ■ ■ ■ ■ Details ■ ■ ■ ■ ■ ■ ■ ■ ■ ■ ■ ■</td></tr>
</table>

I found this on page __220__ .

🔑 **Restate** Boyle's Law.

Pressure of a gas increases if the volume decreases, and pressure of a gas decreases if the volume increases, when temperature is constant.

Temperature and Volume
I found this on page __221__ .

Relate *temperature to volume of gas.*

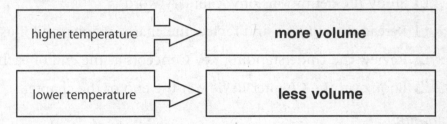

| higher temperature | ⇒ | **more volume** |
| lower temperature | ⇒ | **less volume** |

Charles's Law
I found this on page __222__ .

🔑 **Paraphrase** *the principle represented by the graph if the gas is at a constant* pressure.

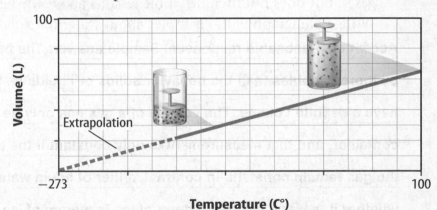

The graph represents Charles's Law. Volume increases with increasing temperature; volume decreases with decreasing temperature.

🔑 **Analyze It** Explain the design of the type of gas container shown in the illustrations and graphs in Lesson 3.

Accept all reasonable responses. Sample answer: The container is enclosed so that the gas being measured does not escape into the air. It has a plunger top, which is pushed upward by the pressure of the gas to indicate the volume the gas occupies in the container. The container is often shown with a weight sitting on top of the plunger to measure the pressure of the gas.

Chapter Wrap-Up

Now that you have read the chapter, think about what you have learned. Complete the final column in the chart on the first page of this chapter.

Use this checklist to help you study.

❏ Complete your Foldables® Chapter Project.

❏ Study your *Science Notebook* on this chapter.

❏ Study the definitions of vocabulary words.

❏ Reread the chapter, and review the charts, graphs, and illustrations.

❏ Review the Understanding Key Concepts at the end of each lesson.

❏ Look over the Chapter Review at the end of the chapter.

THE BIG IDEA

Summarize It Reread the chapter Big Idea and the lesson Key Concepts. Why do you think the chapter includes an entire lesson, Lesson 3, about the behavior of gases, but does not include whole lessons about the behavior of solids and liquids? Write a paragraph with examples about water to explain your answer.

Accept all reasonable responses. Sample answer: The behavior of gases is affected

by more variables than the behavior solids or liquids is. Solids and liquids both

have a definite volume. The volume of a gas can only be measured in a closed

container, and that measurement is only constant if the temperature and pressure of

the gas remain constant. In contrast, a liter of liquid water is still a liter of water

whether it is warm or cold; a gram of ice is a gram of ice, regardless of its shape.

_____

_____

_____

_____

Challenge *Do research to determine a type of matter other than water that people use in a gaseous, liquid, and solid state. Write a summary report about the substance and its properties and behaviors in all three states. Read your report to your class.*

Understanding the Atom

 What are atoms, and what are they made of?

Before You Read

Before you read the chapter, think about what you know about atoms. Record your ideas in the first column. Pair with a partner, and discuss his or her thoughts. Write those ideas in the second column. Then record what you both would like to share with the class in the third column.

Think	Pair	Share

Chapter Vocabulary

Lesson 1	Lesson 2
NEW	**NEW**
atom	atomic number
electron	isotope
nucleus	mass number
proton	average atomic mass
neutron	radioactive
electron cloud	nuclear decay
	ion
	ACADEMIC
	spontaneous

A Lesson Content Vocabulary page for each lesson is provided in the Chapter Resources Files.

> **Predict** *three facts that will be discussed in Lesson 1 after reading the headings. Record your predictions in your Science Journal.*

▪▪▪ **Main Idea** ▪▪▪

▪▪▪▪▪▪▪▪▪▪▪▪▪ **Details** ▪▪▪▪▪▪▪▪▪▪▪▪▪

Early Ideas About Matter

I found this on page ___236___ .

Contrast *ideas about matter held by Greek philosophers.*

	Democritus	**Aristotle**
Ideas About Matter	· matter made of atoms that cannot be divided, created, or destroyed · atoms constantly moving in empty space · different types of matter made of different types of atoms · properties of matter determined by the properties of the atoms	all matter made of four elements: · earth · air · fire · water
Acceptance of Ideas	not studied for over 2,000 years	accepted by people because of Aristotle's popularity

Dalton's Atomic Model

I found this on page ___236___ .

Restate *theories in Dalton's atomic model.*

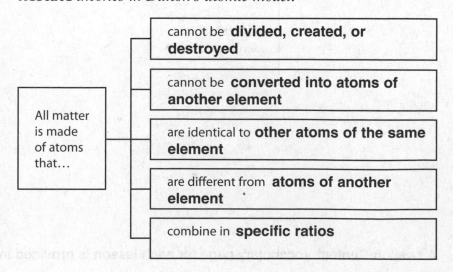

All matter is made of atoms that…

- cannot be **divided, created, or destroyed**
- cannot be **converted into atoms of another element**
- are identical to **other atoms of the same element**
- are different from **atoms of another element**
- combine in **specific ratios**

Lesson 1 | Discovering Parts of an Atom (continued)

■■■ **Main Idea** ■■■ | ■■■■■■■■■■■■■ **Details** ■■■■■■■■■■■■■

The Atom
I found this on page __237__ .

🔑 **Describe** *how present scientists characterize the* atom.

Definition:
smallest piece of an element that still represents the element

Location of empty space:
within and between atoms

Atom

Size:
varies, but all are very, very small

Made of:
much smaller particles

Thompson—Discovering Electrons

🔑 **Sequence** *the discovery of the* electron *and the development of Thompson's atomic model.*

I found this on page __238__ .

I found this on page __239__ .

Event	Result or Conclusion
1. Thompson runs electricity through a cathode ray tube from which most of the air was removed.	**Greenish rays travel from one electrode to the other end of the tube.**
2. Thompson places charged plates on either side of the tube.	**The ray bends toward a positively charged plate.** Conclusion: **The rays are negatively charged.**
3. Identical rays made of tiny particles are produced regardless of the type of metal in the electrode.	Conclusion: **Cathode rays are made of small, negatively charged particles. Thompson called these particles electrons.**
4. Thompson proposes a new model of the atom.	Thompson's model: **An atom is a sphere with positive charge evenly spread throughout, balanced with negative electrons within it.**

■■■ **Main Idea** ■■■ | ■■■■■■■■■■■ **Details** ■■■■■■■■■■■

Rutherford—Discovering the Nucleus

🔑➤ **Sequence** *the discovery of the* nucleus *and the development of Rutherford's atomic model.*

I found this on page ___240___ .

I found this on page ___241___ .

I found this on page ___242___ .

Event	Description
1. Experiment to test Thompson's atomic model	**Rutherford and his students predict that alpha particles will pass through gold foil in a straight line.**
2. Result of the gold foil experiment	**Some particles bounce back or off in all directions.**
3. Conclusion	**The alpha particles must have struck something dense and positively charged.**
4. Description of the dense, positive mass	**The nucleus is made of protons, positively charged particles.**
5. New model of the atom	**An atom has a small, dense, positive nucleus; tiny, negatively charged electrons travel around the nucleus in empty space.**
6. Results of further research	**The positive charge in the nucleus is made up of positively charged particles called protons.**

Discovering Neutrons
I found this on page ___243___ .

Describe *Chadwick's addition to Rutherford's atomic model.*

The nucleus contains neutrons in addition to protons.

Bohr's Atomic Model
I found this on page ___243___ .

Contrast *Bohr's model of the* atom *with Rutherford's model.*

Rutherford	Bohr
Electrons travel in empty space around the nucleus.	**Electrons move around the nucleus in circular orbits at different energy levels.**

▪▪▪ **Main Idea** ▪▪▪ | ▪▪▪▪▪▪▪▪▪▪ **Details** ▪▪▪▪▪▪▪▪▪▪

I found this on page ___243___ .

Diagram *and label* electron *energy levels in Bohr's model.*

Student drawings should show rings representing energy levels around a nucleus. They should designate those closer to the nucleus as lower energy levels and those farther from the nucleus as higher energy levels.

The Modern Atomic Model

I found this on page ___244___ .

🔑 **Contrast** *the location of* electrons *in the modern atomic model with their placement in Bohr's atomic model.*

Bohr Electrons move around the nucleus in circular orbits at different energy levels.	**Modern** **Electrons move in an area around an atomic nucleus called the electron cloud.**

Quarks

I found this on page ___244___ .

Identify *6 types of quarks.*

1. ___up___ 3. ___down___ 5. ___charm___

2. ___strange___ 4. ___top___ 6. ___bottom___

I found this on page ___244___ .

Review *details about particles that make up* atoms.

Particle	Smaller Parts
Electron	**no smaller particle**
Nucleus	**proton, neutron**
Proton	**two up quarks, one down quark**
Neutron	**two down quarks, one up quark**

🔑 **Connect It** Summarize three analogies used in Lesson 1 to describe atoms and the particles that they are made of.

Accept all reasonable responses. Sample answer: In Thompson's model, the atom resembles a chocolate chip cookie. In Rutherford's gold foil experiment, alpha particles shot through atoms would be like throwing a heavy baseball through a pile of light table tennis balls. Electrons in the electron cloud are likened to a swarm of bees around a hive.

> **Skim** *Lesson 2 in your book. Read the headings and look at the photos and illustrations. Identify three things you want to learn more about as you read the lesson. Record your ideas in your Science Journal.*

▪▪▪ **Main Idea** ▪▪▪

▪▪▪▪▪▪▪▪▪▪ **Details** ▪▪▪▪▪▪▪▪▪▪

The Parts of the Atom
I found this on page _____248_____ .

Distinguish *parts of the atom.*

Part	Electron	Proton	Neutron
Symbol	e–	p	n
Charge	1–	1+	0
Location	electron cloud	nucleus	nucleus
Relative Mass	1/1,840	1	1

Different Elements— Different Numbers of Protons
I found this on page _____249_____ .

Relate *details about* atomic number.

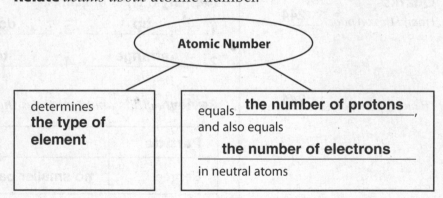

Atomic Number

determines **the type of element**

equals __the number of protons__, and also equals __the number of electrons__ in neutral atoms

Neutrons and Isotopes
I found this on page _____250_____ .

Differentiate *numbers of protons and neutrons in different isotopes of the same element.*

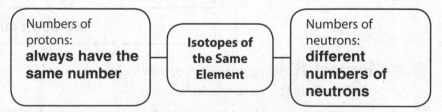

Numbers of protons: **always have the same number**

Isotopes of the Same Element

Numbers of neutrons: **different numbers of neutrons**

I found this on page _____250_____ .

Contrast *the numbers of particles represented by an element's* mass number *and* atomic number.

Atomic Number	Mass Number
same as the number of protons	the sum of the number of protons and neutrons

▪▪▪ **Main Idea** ▪▪▪ | ▪▪▪▪▪▪▪▪▪▪▪▪▪ **Details** ▪▪▪▪▪▪▪▪▪▪▪▪▪

I found this on page __251__ .

Define average atomic mass.

the average mass of an element's isotopes, weighted

according to the abundance of each isotope

Radioactivity

I found this on page __253__ .

🔑 **Differentiate** *three types of* nuclear decay *that occur in* radioactive *elements*.

Type	Change	Result
Alpha decay	two protons and two neutrons	new element; atomic number decreased by two
Beta decay	neutron becomes a proton; beta particle is released	new element; atomic number increases by one
Gamma decay	release of gamma rays	same element; no change in protons or neutrons

Ions—Gaining or Losing Electrons

I found this on page __254__ .

🔑 **Contrast** *the formation of* ions.

Positive Ion	Negative Ion
A neutral atom **loses one or more electrons** .	A neutral atom **gains one or more electrons** .
Result: **The atom has a positive charge** .	Result: **The atom has a negative charge** .

🔑 **Synthesize It** Summarize why people were unsuccessful over 1,000 years ago when they tried to transform lead into gold. What process would they have needed to complete in order to have been successful?

Accept all reasonable responses. Sample answer: In order to change lead into gold,

people would have had to remove three protons from the nucleus of each lead atom.

They did not have the technology to make this change in the lead atoms.

Chapter Wrap-Up

Now that you have read the chapter, think about what you have learned.

Use this checklist to help you study.

❏ Complete your Foldables® Chapter Project.

❏ Study your *Science Notebook* on this chapter.

❏ Study the definitions of vocabulary words.

❏ Reread the chapter, and review the charts, graphs, and illustrations.

❏ Review the Understanding Key Concepts at the end of each lesson.

❏ Look over the Chapter Review at the end of the chapter.

 Summarize It Reread the chapter Big Idea and the lesson Key Concepts. Summarize how each scientist contributed to the history of scientific understanding of atoms.

Aristotle: **Popularized the idea that all matter was made of combinations of earth, air, fire, and water.**

Democritus: **Theorized that matter was made of tiny particles with the properties of the matter.**

Dalton: **Theorized that matter was made of atoms, the smallest parts of elements that could not be created, destroyed, or changed.**

Thompson: **Discovered that atoms contained negative particles, electrons; theorized there must be a sphere of positive charge in the atom with electrons throughout.**

Rutherford: **Established that atoms have a dense, positively charged nucleus surrounded by electrons moving in mostly empty space.**

Chadwick: **Described the presence of neutrons along with protons in the nucleus to account for the mass of the atom.**

Bohr: **Modified Rutherford's atomic model by describing electron energy levels.**

Becquerel and the Curies: **Observed and described radioactivity.**

Challenge *Do research to learn more about the Large Hadron Collider experiments at CERN. Write a short news article that summarizes how the largest machine ever built is expected to reveal the tiniest particles in the universe. Share your article with your class.*

Name _____ Date _____

Elements and Chemical Bonds

 How do elements join together to form chemical compounds?

Before You Read

Before you read the chapter, think about what you know about elements and chemical bonds. Record your thoughts in the first column. Pair with a partner, and discuss his or her thoughts. Write those thoughts in the second column. Then record what you both would like to share with the class in the third column.

Think	Pair	Share

Chapter Vocabulary

Lesson 1	Lesson 2	Lesson 3
NEW chemical bond valence electron electron dot diagram	**NEW** chemical formula covalent bond molecule polar molecule	**NEW** ion ionic bond metallic bond
REVIEW compound		**ACADEMIC** conduct

A Lesson Content Vocabulary page for each lesson is provided in the Chapter Resources Files.

Scan *Lesson 1. Record three questions you have about electrons and energy levels in your Science Journal. Try to answer your questions as you read.*

=== **Main Idea** === | === **Details** ===

The Periodic Table

I found this on page ____267____ .

Describe *characteristics of the periodic table.*

Characteristic	Description
Atomic number	the number of protons in an atom of the element
Atomic mass	the average mass of all of the different isotopes of the element
Period	a row of elements
Group	a column of elements
Metals	the elements arranged on the left side of the periodic table, except H
Metalloids	the elements arranged in a stair-step pattern between metals and nonmetals
Nonmetals	the elements on the right side of the periodic table, plus hydrogen

I found this on page ____268____ .

Atoms Bond

I found this on page ____268____ .

Describe compounds.

Compounds are composed of atoms of two or more

elements held together by chemical bonds.

I found this on page ____269____ .

🔑 **Summarize** *the relationship between an electron's energy level and its location in an atom. Circle the word that makes each statement true.*

The closer to the nucleus, the	The farther from the nucleus, the
(lower) / higher	lower / (higher)
an electron's energy level.	an electron's energy level.

Lesson 1 | Electrons and Energy Levels (continued)

■■■ **Main Idea** ■■■

I found this on page ___269___ .

Drawings should show 6 "+" and 6 "n" in the center circle, 2 "–" on the inner dashed line, and 4 "–" on the outer dashed line.

I found this on page ___270___ .

I found this on page ___271___ .

■■■■■■■■■■■ **Details** ■■■■■■■■■■■

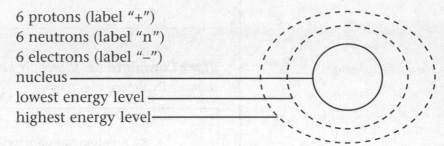 **Model** *the structure of an atom. Use the labels listed below to indicate the location of protons, neutrons, and electrons. Draw lines from the labels to indicate the position of the nucleus, the lowest energy level, and the highest energy level.*

6 protons (label "+")
6 neutrons (label "n")
6 electrons (label "–")
nucleus
lowest energy level
highest energy level

Analyze *details about* valence electrons.

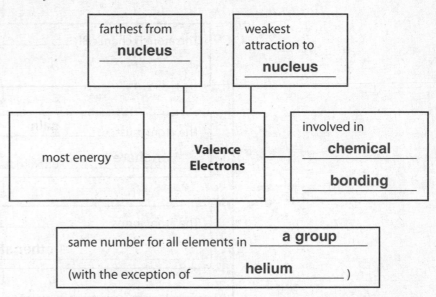

farthest from **nucleus**

weakest attraction to **nucleus**

most energy

Valence Electrons

involved in **chemical bonding**

same number for all elements in ___a group___

(with the exception of ___helium___)

Sequence *the steps in constructing and interpreting an* electron dot diagram.

❶ Identify the element's ___group number___ .

❷ Identify the number of ___valence electrons___ , which is the same as the ___ones digit___ of the ___group number___ .

❸ Place ___one___ dot at a time on each ___side___ of the ___element symbol___ . Pair up the dots until all are used.

❹ Identify an atom as ___stable___ if all ___dots___ are ___paired___ .

❺ Count the ___unpaired dots___ to determine how many ___bonds___ an unstable atom can form.

Main Idea

I found this on page __272__ .

I found this on page __272__ .

Details

Explain *why noble gases are stable.*

All noble gases (except helium) have eight valence

electrons, so all of their valence electrons are paired.

🔑 **Complete** *the flowchart about the behavior of atoms with* *unpaired* valence electrons.

An atom has unpaired valence electrons.

↓

The atom is chemically ____**unstable**____.

↓

The atom must ____**gain**____, ____**lose**____, or ____**share**____ unpaired ____**electrons**____.

↓

The atom forms ____**bonds**____ with ____**other atom(s)**____.

↓

When an atom's ____**unpaired valence electrons**____ become ____**paired**____, the atom becomes ____**stable**____.

🔑 **Analyze It** Use what you have learned in Lesson 1 to explain why elements are rarely found in their pure forms.

Accept all reasonable responses. Sample answer: Atoms of most elements are

unstable because they have unpaired valence electrons. Therefore, they have a

strong tendency to bond with other atoms and form compounds with completed

electron pairs.

Predict *three facts that will be discussed in Lesson 2 after reading the headings. Record your predictions in your Science Journal.*

▪▪▪ **Main Idea** ▪▪▪

▪▪▪▪▪ **Details** ▪▪▪▪▪

From Elements to Compounds

🔑 **Recall** *information about elements and compounds. Read each statement. If it is true, write T in the center column. If it is false, write F in the center column and rewrite the underlined words to make the statement true.*

I found this on page ___276___ .

I found this on page ___276___ .

I found this on page ___276___ .

Statement	T or F	Correction
<u>Compounds</u> are chemical combinations of <u>elements</u>.	T	
Compounds <u>usually</u> have the same properties as the <u>bonds</u> they are made from.	F	**seldom, elements**
Atoms form bonds by sharing <u>physical</u> <u>properties</u>.	F	**valence electrons**

I found this on page ___280___ .

Define chemical formula.

A chemical formula is a group of symbols and numbers

that represent the elements and the number of atoms of

each element that compose a compound

I found this on page ___280___ .

Explain *the chemical formula for a molecule of water. Describe what each symbol represents.*

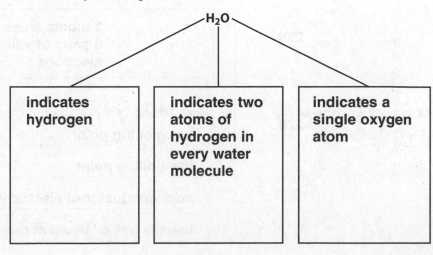

H_2O

| indicates hydrogen | indicates two atoms of hydrogen in every water molecule | indicates a single oxygen atom |

▪▪▪ **Main Idea** ▪▪▪

| ▪▪▪▪▪▪▪▪▪▪▪▪ **Details** ▪▪▪▪▪▪▪▪▪▪▪▪

I found this on page __280__ .

Identify *four types of molecular models.*

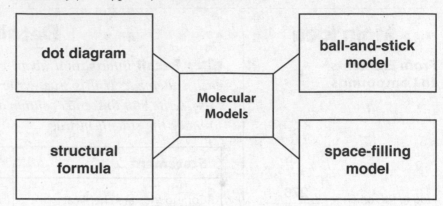

Covalent Bonds— Electron Sharing

I found this on page __277__ .

Define covalent bond.

a chemical bond formed when two nonmetal atoms share

one or more pairs of valence electrons

Describe *types of* covalent bonds.

I found this on page __277__ .

I found this on page __278__ .

I found this on page __278__ .

Covalent Bond	Description of Valence Electron Sharing	Comment on the Strength of the Bond
Single	2 atoms share 1 pair of valance electrons	weakest type of covalent bond
Double	2 atoms share 2 pairs of valance electrons	stronger than single covalent bonds
Triple	2 atoms share 3 pairs of valance electrons	stronger than double covalent bonds

Covalent Compounds
I found this on page __278__ .

🔑 **Identify** *4 common properties of covalent compounds.*

1. low melting point

2. low boiling point

3. poor conductor of electricity or thermal energy

4. usually gas or liquid at room temperature

Lesson 2 | Compounds, Chemical Formulas, and Covalent Bonds (continued)

▪▪▪ Main Idea ▪▪▪

I found this on page ___278___ .

I found this on page ___279___ .

I found this on page ___279___ .

I found this on page ___279___ .

I found this on page ___279___ .

▪▪▪▪▪▪▪▪ Details ▪▪▪▪▪▪▪▪

Complete *the analogy.*

| Atom is to element as ___molecule___ is to compound. |

Summarize *the structure of* polar molecules.

| ___unequal___ sharing of ___electrons___ results in | → | a partial ___positive end___ and a partial ___negative end___ | → | polar molecule |

🔑➤ **Explain** *why water is a* polar molecule.

Water molecules are polar because the negative electrons

are more strongly attracted to the oxygen atom, leaving a

slightly positive charge near the hydrogen atoms.

Differentiate polar *and nonpolar* molecules *with regard to shared electrons.*

Polar Molecules	Nonpolar Molecules
Electrons are shared unequally.	Electrons are shared equally.

Relate *the saying "like dissolves like" to the ability of compounds to dissolve one another.*

Sample answer: Polar compounds can dissolve in other

polar compounds, and nonpolar compounds can dissolve

in other nonpolar compounds, but polar and nonpolar

compounds do not dissolve in each other.

🔑➤ **Connect It** Explain why there are many more covalent compounds than there are pure elements.

Accept all reasonable responses. Sample answer: There are several combinations of

possible ways that valence electrons can be shared, and unstable atoms have a

tendency to bond in order to become more stable.

Scan *Lesson 3. Read the lesson titles and bold words. Look at the pictures. Identify three facts you discovered about ionic and metallic bonds. Record your facts in your Science Journal.*

■■■ **Main Idea** ■■■ | ■■■■■■■■ **Details** ■■■■■■■■

Understanding Ions
I found this on page _____284_____ .

Organize *information about* ions.

An atom gains an electron	→	Overall charge becomes _____negative_____
An atom loses an electron	→	Overall charge becomes _____positive_____

I found this on page _____285_____ .

Analyze *what happens to sodium and chlorine atoms in the formation of the compound sodium chloride.*

	Na (sodium)	**Cl** (chlorine)
Type of element	metal	nonmetal
Atomic number	11	17
Number of valence electrons	1	7
Stable or unstable?	unstable	unstable
Electron transfer	1 lost	1 gained
Description after transfer	stable, 10 electrons like neon	stable, 18 electrons like argon
Type of ion	positive (+)	negative (−)

Ionic Bonds—Electron Transferring
I found this on page _____286_____ .

Complete *the diagram of an* ionic bond.

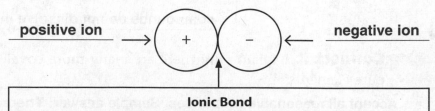

positive ion → (+)(−) ← negative ion

Ionic Bond

Explanation: The oppositely charged ions attract one

another and form an ionic compound.

▪▪▪ **Main Idea** ▪▪▪

▪▪▪▪▪▪▪▪▪▪▪ **Details** ▪▪▪▪▪▪▪▪▪▪▪▪

Ionic Compounds
I found this on page ____286____ .
Sample answers are shown.

🔑 **Identify** *five common properties of ionic compounds.*

1. ions strongly attracted to each other

2. good conductors of electricity when in water

3. usually solid at room temperature

4. high melting point

5. high boiling point

Metallic Bonds—Electron Pooling
I found this on page ____287____ .

Explain *how a* metallic bond *forms.*

A metallic bond forms when many metal atoms share their

pooled valence electrons.

I found this on page ____288____ .
Sample answers are shown.

Describe *three properties of metallic compounds.*

Properties of Metallic Compounds

| high melting and boiling points | good conductors of thermal energy and electricity | can be hammered into sheets or pulled into wires |

I found this on page ____287____ .

🔑 **Contrast** *3 ways atoms can bond and become stable.*

Process	Electron Pooling	Electron Transfer	Electron Sharing
Type of chemical bond	metallic	ionic	covalent
Description	Valence electrons of metal atoms are not bonded to any one atom.	Valence electrons are transferred from nonmetal to metal atoms.	Valence electrons are shared by nonmetal atoms.

🔑 **Analyze It** Explain the difference between a neutral atom and a stable atom.

An atom is stable if its highest energy level contains the maximum number of paired

electrons. An atom is electrically neutral if it has the same number of protons and

electrons, the positive and negative charges of which balance.

Elements and Chemical Bonds

Chapter Wrap-Up

Now that you have read the chapter, think about what you have learned.

Use this checklist to help you study.

❏ Complete your Foldables® Chapter Project.

❏ Study your *Science Notebook* on this chapter.

❏ Study the definitions of vocabulary words.

❏ Reread the chapter, and review the charts, graphs, and illustrations.

❏ Review the Understanding Key Concepts at the end of each lesson.

❏ Look over the Chapter Review at the end of the chapter.

THE BIG IDEA

Summarize It Reread the chapter Big Idea and the lesson Key Concepts. Use what you have learned to describe why it is important in the modern world to understand the types of chemical bonds and the properties of types of compounds. Give at least one example.

Accept all reasonable responses. Sample answer: All the technologies we rely on in

modern society are made of matter that behaves in certain ways. The way matter

behaves determines what it can be used for; for example, our electrical circuits are

made of metal because metal can be pulled into wire and is a good conductor of

electricity. The pooling of electrons in metallic bonding allows the metal to be

flexible. Because valence electrons can move easily from atom to atom, they can

carry an electric charge.

_____

_____

_____

_____

_____

Challenge *Research the uses of noble gases in technological devices. Why do the properties of the gases make them useful? Summarize your discoveries in your Science Journal.*

Chemical Reactions and Equations

What happens to atoms and energy during a chemical reaction?

Before You Read

Before you read the chapter, think about what you know about chemical reactions. Record three things that you already know about chemical reactions in the first column. Then write three things that you would like to learn about in the second column. Complete the final column of the chart when you have finished this chapter.

| K
What I Know | W
What I Want to Learn | L
What I Learned |
|---|---|---|
| | | |

Chapter Vocabulary

Lesson 1	Lesson 2	Lesson 3
NEW
chemical reaction
chemical equation
reactant
product
law of conservation
   of mass
coefficient

REVIEW
chemical bond | **NEW**
synthesis
decomposition
single replacement
double replacement
combustion | **NEW**
endothermic
exothermic
activation energy
catalyst
enzyme
inhibitor |

A Lesson Content Vocabulary page for each lesson is provided in the Chapter Resources Files.

▪▪▪ **Main Idea** ▪▪▪   ▪▪▪▪▪▪▪▪▪▪ **Details** ▪▪▪▪▪▪▪▪▪▪

Changes in Matter

I found this on page ___301___ .

Differentiate *a physical change from a chemical change.*

Physical Change	Chemical Change
New substances are not produced, but the substances that exist before and after the change might have different physical properties.	One or more substances change into new substances with different physical and chemical properties.

Signs of a Chemical Reaction

I found this on page ___302___ .

🔑 **Identify** *signs of a chemical reaction.*

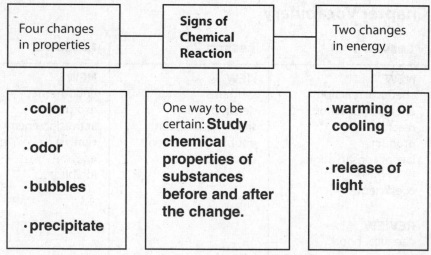

Four changes in properties	Signs of Chemical Reaction	Two changes in energy
· **color** · **odor** · **bubbles** · **precipitate**	One way to be certain: **Study chemical properties of substances before and after the change.**	· **warming or cooling** · **release of light**

What happens during a chemical reaction?

I found this on page ___303___ .

🔑 **Sequence** *changes in atoms during a* **chemical reaction.**

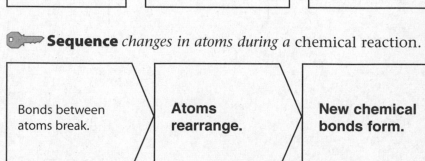

Bonds between atoms break.	**Atoms rearrange.**	**New chemical bonds form.**

Lesson 1 | Understanding Chemical Reactions (continued)

Chemical Equations
I found this on page ___304___ .

🔑 **Distinguish** *the parts of a* chemical equation.

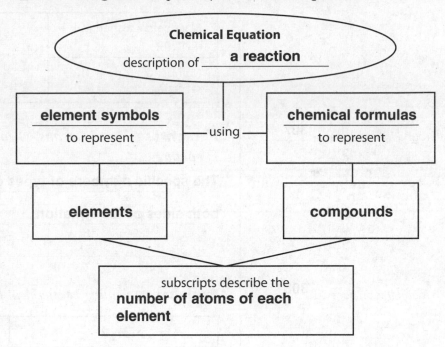

I found this on page ___305___ .

Detail *information regarding the writing of* chemical equations.

Define *reactant*.	**the starting substances in a chemical reaction**
Define *product*.	**the substances produced by a chemical reaction**
Write the general structure for a chemical equation.	**reactant + reactant ⟶ product + product**
How is the arrow sign read?	**as "produces" or "yields"**
Write the equation for "carbon plus oxygen produces carbon dioxide."	**$C + O_2 \longrightarrow CO_2$**

Conservation of Mass
I found this on page ___306___ .

🔑 **Restate** *the* law of conservation of mass.

The total mass before a chemical reaction is the same as

the total mass after a chemical reaction.

▪▪▪ **Main Idea** ▪▪▪	▪▪▪▪▪▪▪▪▪▪▪▪ **Details** ▪▪▪▪▪▪▪▪▪▪▪▪

I found this on page __306__ .

🔑 **Relate** *atoms to mass in a* chemical reaction.

Mass before a chemical reaction	is equal to	**mass after a chemical reaction**
Number of atoms in the reactants		**number of atoms in the products**

I found this on page __307__ .

Paraphrase *what it means when you say a* chemical equation *is balanced.*

The specific numbers of types of atoms are the same on

both sides of the equation.

_____

I found this on page __308__ .

Explain *the meaning of chemical formulas.* Circle the coefficient.

H₂O	**②H₂O**
means **one water molecule**	means **two water molecules**

I found this on page __308__ .

Order *the steps in balancing a* chemical equation.

1. Write the unbalanced equation.

2. Count atoms of each element in the reactants and

   products.

3. Add coefficients to balance the atoms.

4. Write the balanced chemical equation.

I found this on page __308__ .

Balance *the chemical equation for carbon monoxide.*

$$2\,C \ + \ O_2 \longrightarrow \ 2\,CO$$

🔑 **Analyze It** Look back at the picture of the firefly on the first page of Lesson 1. How could you conclude that the firefly's blinking is a chemical rather than a physical change simply by viewing the picture and without reading the text on the page?

Accept all reasonable responses. Sample answer: The firefly's blink gives off light

energy. The release of light is an energy change, which is characteristic of a chemical

change, not a physical change.

Predict *three facts that will be discussed in Lesson 2 after reading the headings. Write your facts in your Science Journal.*

▪▪▪ Main Idea ▪▪▪

Patterns in Reactions
I found this on page ___312___ .

Types of Chemical Reactions
I found this on page ___313___ .

▪▪▪▪▪▪▪▪▪▪ Details ▪▪▪▪▪▪▪▪▪▪

Generalize *the concept of patterns in chemical reactions.*

| Number of types: 4 | Major Types of Chemical Reactions | Determined by: the way atoms recombine |

🔑 **Describe and model** synthesis *and* decomposition reactions. First, describe the reactions. Then draw simple shapes to model how substances behave during these reactions.

	Synthesis	Decomposition
Explanation	Two or more substances combine and form one compound.	One compound breaks down and forms two or more substances.
Diagram	Student drawing should show different shapes for two or more elements on the left side of the equation and the shapes side by side to represent a single compound on the right side of the equation.	Student drawing should show different shapes side by side to represent a single compound on the left side of the equation and the shapes separated to represent two or more elements on the right side of the equation.

■■■ **Main Idea** ■■■ | ■■■■■■■■■ **Details** ■■■■■■■■■

I found this on page ___314___.

🔑 **Describe** *replacement reactions. Include a model of* single- *and* double-replacement *reactions with your descriptions.*

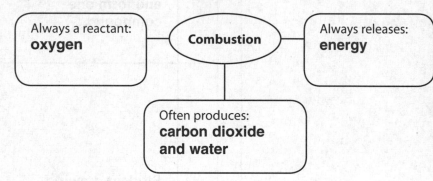

Replacement Reactions
An atom or group of atoms replaces part of a compound.

Single-replacement
One element replaces another element in a compound.

● ■ + ▲ ➞ ● ▲ + ■

Double-replacement
The negative ions in two compounds switch places.

● ■ + ▲ ✳ ➞ ● ✳ + ▲ ■

I found this on page ___314___.

🔑 **Characterize** combustion.

Always a reactant:
oxygen

Combustion

Always releases:
energy

Often produces:
carbon dioxide and water

I found this on page ___314___.

Identify *the two types of energy typically released during* combustion *reactions.*

1. **thermal energy**

2. **light energy**

🔑 **Synthesize It** Summarize the four major types of chemical reactions you learned about in Lesson 2.

Synthesis reactions combine two or more elements or compounds into one

compound; decomposition breaks one compound into two or more substances. In

replacement reactions, component parts of compounds recombine to form different

compounds. Combustion always involves oxygen as a reactant and releases energy.

Lesson 3 Energy Changes and Chemical Reactions

Skim *Lesson 3 in your book. Read the headings and look at the photos and illustrations. Identify three things you want to learn more about as you read the lesson. Record your ideas in your Science Journal.*

▪▪▪ **Main Idea** ▪▪▪ | ▪▪▪▪▪▪▪▪▪▪▪ **Details** ▪▪▪▪▪▪▪▪▪▪

Energy Changes
I found this on page ____318____.

🔑 **Expand** *the model of a chemical reaction to represent energy changes that occur.*

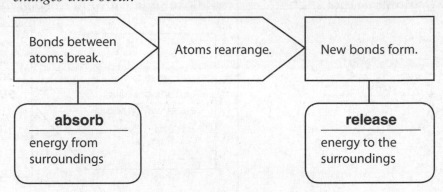

I found this on page ____319____.

🔑 **Differentiate** endothermic *and* exothermic *reactions.*

Reaction	reactants + thermal energy ⟶ products
Type	**endothermic**
Energy change	**thermal energy absorbed**
Bonds that contain more energy	**products**
Reaction	reactants ⟶ thermal energy + products
Type	**exothermic**
Energy change	**thermal energy released**
Bonds that contain more energy	**reactants**

I found this on page ____320____.

Define activation energy, *and identify types of reactions that use it.*

Activation energy: __the minimum amount of energy needed__

__to start a chemical reaction__

Types of reactions: __both exothermic and endothermic__

Main Idea

Details

Reaction Rates

I found this on page ___320___ .

🔑 **Record** *two factors about particle collisions that affect the rate of chemical reactions.*

1. how often particles collide

2. how fast particles are moving when they collide

I found this on page ___321___ .

Relate *surface area to reaction rate in the following example.*

A chunk of chalk reacts with vinegar.

Speed of reaction rate: **slower**
Explanation: **Acid is in contact only with particles on the surface of the chalk.**

Crushed chalk powder reacts with vinegar.

Speed of reaction rate: **faster**
Explanation: **More chalk particles are in contact with the acid.**

I found this on page ___321___ .

🔑 **Distinguish** *two reasons that higher temperature speeds reaction rate.*

Higher Temperature

Average speed of particles increases, so particles collide more often.

Collisions have more energy and are more likely to break chemical bonds.

▪▪▪ **Main Idea** ▪▪▪ | ▪▪▪▪▪▪▪▪▪▪▪▪▪▪ **Details** ▪▪▪▪▪▪▪▪▪▪▪▪▪▪

I found this on page _____321_____ .

Compare *higher concentration and increased pressure as means to increase reaction rate.*

In both situations, particles are closer together, which

causes more collisions between particles to occur.

_____

I found this on page _____322_____ .

Relate *the presence of a* catalyst *in a chemical reaction to* activation energy *and reaction rate.*

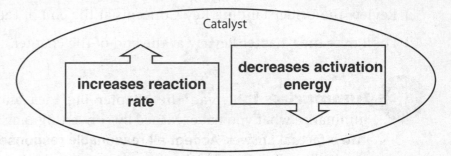

I found this on page _____322_____ .

Express *the relationship between* catalysts *and* enzymes.

An enzyme is a type of catalyst. It speeds up chemical

reactions in living cells.

I found this on page _____322_____ .

Contrast catalysts *and* inhibitors

	Catalyst	Inhibitor
Description	increases reaction rate by lowering activation energy	slows, or even stops, a chemical reaction

🔑 **Connect It** Consider the example of the rocket launch shown in the picture on the first page of Lesson 3. Hypothesize why it would be important to understand both catalysts and inhibitors in this series of chemical reactions.

Accept all reasonable responses. Sample answer: A rocket launch requires a massive

amount of energy to be released rapidly, so catalysts that speed the reaction are

helpful. However, rocket fuel sources can react so quickly, in fact, that they can be

highly explosive. Inhibitors keep the fuel under control until the right time.

Chemical Reactions and Equations

Chapter Wrap-Up

Now that you have read the chapter, think about what you have learned. Complete the final column in the chart on the first page of the chapter.

Use this checklist to help you study.

❏ Complete your Foldables® Chapter Project.

❏ Study your *Science Notebook* on this chapter.

❏ Study the definitions of vocabulary words.

❏ Reread the chapter, and review the charts, graphs, and illustrations.

❏ Review the Understanding Key Concepts at the end of each lesson.

❏ Look over the Chapter Review at the end of the chapter.

THE BIG IDEA **Summarize It** Reread the chapter Big Idea and the lesson Key Concepts. Summarize what you have learned by converting each of the Key Concept questions into a factual answer. **Accept all reasonable responses. Sample answers:**

Lesson 1 (three Key Concepts)

1. Warming or cooling and the release of light are some signs that a chemical

reaction might have occurred. 2. Atoms are conserved during a chemical reaction.

3. Total mass is conserved in a chemical reaction.

Lesson 2 (two Key Concepts)

1. You can recognize a synthesis reaction by the multiple reactants that combine to

form one compound as a product. 2. The four main types of chemical reactions are

synthesis, decomposition, replacement, and combustion.

Lesson 3 (three Key Concepts)

1. Chemical reactions always involve a change in energy because chemical bonds

contain chemical energy. 2. The difference between endothermic and exothermic

reactions is that endothermic reactions absorb energy and exothermic reactions

release energy. 3. Surface area, temperature, and pressure affect the rate of a

chemical reaction.

Challenge *Choose a chemical reaction that you routinely observe. This could be anything from rust forming on playground equipment, to photosynthesis in grass, to the combustion of fuel in your family's car. Make an illustrated poster that describes the reactants, products, and energy processes in the reaction. Be sure to use balanced chemical equations in your captions. Display your poster in your class.*

Mixtures, Solubility, and Acid/Base Solutions

 What are solutions, and how are they described?

Before You Read

Before you read the chapter, think about what you know about mixtures and solutions. Record your ideas in the first column. Pair with a partner, and discuss his or her thoughts. Write those ideas in the second column. Then record what you both would like to share with the class in the third column.

Think	Pair	Share

Chapter Vocabulary

Lesson 1	Lesson 2	Lesson 3
NEW	**NEW**	**NEW**
substance	solvent	acid
mixture	solute	hydronium ion
heterogeneous mixture	polar molecule	base
homogeneous mixture	concentration	pH
solution	solubility	indicator
	saturated solution	
REVIEW	unsaturated solution	
compound		
	ACADEMIC	
	analogous	

A Lesson Content Vocabulary page for each lesson is provided in the Chapter Resources Files.

Predict *three facts that will be discussed in Lesson 1 after reading the headings. Record your predictions in your Science Journal.*

▪▪▪ Main Idea ▪▪▪ | ▪▪▪▪▪ Details ▪▪▪▪▪

Matter: Substances and Mixtures

I found this on page ___336___ .

🔑 **Differentiate** substances *and* mixtures.

Categories of Matter

Substances

Definition:
matter that is always made up of the same combinations of atoms

Two types:
·elements

·compounds

Mixtures

Definition:
two or more substances that are physically blended but not chemically bonded together

I found this on page ___337___ .

Sample examples are shown.

Contrast heterogeneous mixtures *with* homogeneous mixtures.

Mixture	Description	Examples
Heterogeneous	**Substances are not evenly mixed.**	**· granite** **· blood**
Homogeneous	**Substances are evenly mixed on the atomic level, but are not bonded together.**	**· soda** **· air**

I found this on page ___337___ .

🔑 **Compare** *the definitions of the terms* solution *and* homogeneous mixture.

They mean the same thing. They both are mixtures in

which two or more substances are evenly mixed on the

atomic level, but are not bonded together.

▪▪▪ **Main Idea** ▪▪▪ | ▪▪▪▪▪▪▪▪▪▪▪▪ **Details** ▪▪▪▪▪▪▪▪▪▪▪▪

How do compounds and mixtures differ?

I found this on page ___338___ .

🔑 **Note** *three differences between compounds and* mixtures.

Mixture	Compound
The substances that make it up are not chemically bonded.	Elements that make it up are chemically bonded together.
Substances keep their properties.	Properties can be different from the properties of the elements that make it up.
They can be separated using physical methods.	They can only be separated by a chemical change that breaks bonds.

I found this on page ___339___ .

Characterize *combinations of matter.*

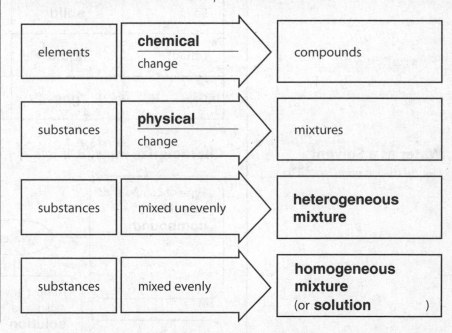

🔑 **Connect It** Explain whether the following sentence is true: All substances are elements, but all elements are not substances.

Accept all reasonable responses. Sample answer: No; it is the other way around. All

elements are substances because they are always made up of the same combination

of atoms. But many substances are compounds, made of atoms of two or more

elements bonded together.

Scan *Lesson 2. Read the lesson titles and bold words. Look at the pictures. Identify three facts you discovered about solutions. Record your facts in your Science Journal.*

■■■ **Main Idea** ■■■ ┊ ■■■■■■■■■■■■■ **Details** ■■■■■■■■■■■■■

Parts of Solutions
I found this on page _____343_____ .

Differentiate solvent *from* solute *in a solution.*

Solvent		Solute
exists in the greatest quantity in a solution		all substances in a solution other than the solvent

Types of Solutions
I found this on page _____344_____ .

Categorize *parts of different types of solutions.*

Type of Solution	Solvent is a	Solute can be
Solid	**solid**	**gas or solid**
Liquid	**liquid**	**solid, liquid, and/or gas**
Gas	**gas**	**gas**

Water as a Solvent
I found this on page _____344_____ .

Characterize *water as it relates to solutions.*

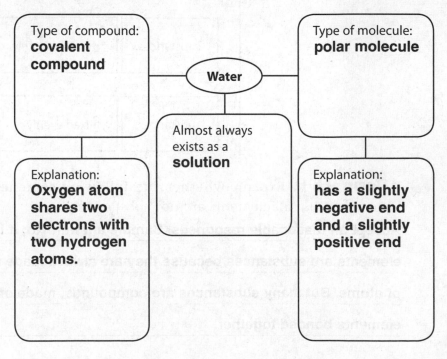

Type of compound: **covalent compound**

Type of molecule: **polar molecule**

Water

Almost always exists as a **solution**

Explanation: **Oxygen atom shares two electrons with two hydrogen atoms.**

Explanation: **has a slightly negative end and a slightly positive end**

Lesson 2 | Properties of Solutions (continued)

▪▪▪ **Main Idea** ▪▪▪ | ▪▪▪▪▪ **Details** ▪▪▪▪▪

Like Dissolves Like

I found this on page ___345___ .

🔑 **Diagram** *the concept of "like dissolves like."*

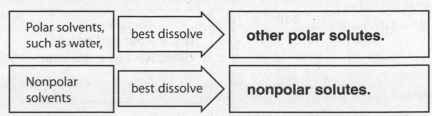

| Polar solvents, such as water, | best dissolve → | **other polar solutes.** |
| Nonpolar solvents | best dissolve → | **nonpolar solutes.** |

I found this on page ___345___ .

🔑 **Model** *the attraction of an ionic compound, NaCl, to a polar solvent, water.*

Student drawing should represent the bent shape of water molecules with a negative charge on the side of the larger oxygen atom and a positive charge on the side of the two smaller hydrogen atoms. The positive ends of the water molecules should present toward negative chloride ions; the negative ends of the water molecules should present toward positive sodium ions.

Concentration—How much is dissolved?

I found this on page ___346___ .

Contrast *concentrated and dilute solutions.*

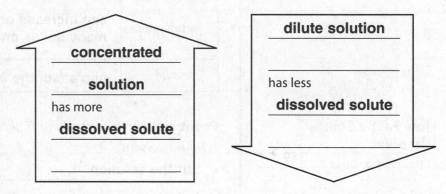

concentrated

solution

has more

dissolved solute

dilute solution

has less

dissolved solute

I found this on page ___347___ .

Represent *concentration in an equation.*

$$\text{Concentration } (C) = \frac{\textbf{mass of solute } (m)}{\textbf{volume of solution } (V)}$$

I found this on page ___347___ .

Describe *the calculation of* concentration *by percent of volume.*

the volume of solute divided by the total volume of the

solution multiplied by 100

▪▪▪ **Main Idea** ▪▪▪ | ▪▪▪▪▪▪▪▪▪▪▪▪ **Details** ▪▪▪▪▪▪▪▪▪▪▪▪

Solubility—How much can dissolve?

I found this on page ____348____ .

🔑 **Contrast** concentration *and* solubility.

| **Concentration**
the amount of solute dissolved in a solution | **Solubility**
the amount of solute an amount of solvent *can* dissolve |

I found this on page ____348____ .

Differentiate saturated solutions *from* unsaturated solutions.

At given __**temperature**__ and __**pressure**__

Saturated solutions contain maximum solute the solvent can hold

Unsaturated solutions can still dissolve more solute

I found this on page ____349____ .

🔑 **Explain** *factors that can affect* solubility.

Factor	Explanation
Temperature	can increase or decrease the solubility of many solids and gases in liquids
Pressure	can affect the solubility of gases in liquids

How Fast a Solute Dissolves

I found this on page ____349____ .

Point out *three methods to make a solid solute dissolve faster in a liquid solvent.*

1. Stir the solution.

2. Crush the solute.

3. Increase the temperature.

🔑 **Analyze It** Describe a solution that you encounter routinely. Use and circle at least five of the Lesson 2 vocabulary words in your description.

Accept all reasonable responses. Sample answer: I drink soda. It is a solution of water, a solvent with polar molecules, and many solutes that give it flavor. It has a high concentration of sugar, but probably is not a saturated solution because I think I could dissolve more sugar in it.

> **Skim** *Lesson 3 in your book. Read the headings and look at the photos and illustrations. Identify three things you want to learn more about as you read the lesson. Record your ideas in your Science Journal.*

▪▪▪ **Main Idea** ▪▪▪ | ▪▪▪▪▪▪▪▪ **Details** ▪▪▪▪▪▪▪▪

What are acids and bases?
I found this on page __354__ .

🔑 **Differentiate** acids *and* bases.

Acid a substance that produces a hydronium ion when dissolved in water	**Base** a substance that produces a hydroxide ion when dissolved in water

I found this on page __355__ .

Categorize *properties and uses of* acids *and* bases. *Place an* **A** *before properties of* acids, *and a* **B** *before properties of* bases. *Note that some properties apply to both.*

____**A**____ provide sour taste in food

____**A**____ found in saliva

__**A and B**__ can damage skin and eyes

____**B**____ OH⁻ ions can conduct electricity

____**A**____ react with metals to produce hydrogen gas

____**B**____ slippery

____**A**____ H_3O^+ ions can conduct electricity

____**B**____ provide bitter taste in food

____**A**____ found in milk

____**A**____ helps plants grow

What is pH?
I found this on page __356__ .

🔑 **Model** *the measure of pH in a solution.*

As the concentration of hydronium ions **increases**

pH **decreases**

Lesson 3 | Acid and Base Solutions (continued)

■■■ Main Idea ■■■ | **■■■■■■■■■ Details ■■■■■■■■■**

I found this on page __356__.

Redraw *the model from the bottom of the previous page to show decreasing concentration of* hydronium ions. *Add a third arrow to show what happens to acidity as this change occurs.*

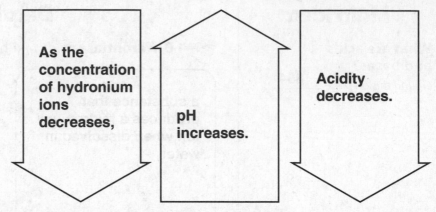

As the concentration of hydronium ions decreases,

pH increases.

Acidity decreases.

I found this on page __357__.

Relate *concentrations of ions to the* pH *of solutions.*

Solutions	Relationship Between Hydronium and Hydroxide Ions	Value on the pH Scale
Acids	$H_3O^+ > OH^-$	<7
Neutral	$H_3O^+ = OH^-$	7
Bases	$H_3O^+ < OH^-$	>7

I found this on page __357__.

Determine *concentrations of* hydronium ions.

pH value	Concentration of Hydronium Ions
3	10,000
4	1,000
5	100
6	10
7	1
8	1/10
9	1/100
10	1/1,000
11	1/10,000

▪▪▪ **Main Idea** ▪▪▪

I found this on page ___357___ .

How is pH measured?

I found this on page ___358___ .

I found this on page ___358___ .

▪▪▪▪▪▪ **Details** ▪▪▪▪▪▪

Represent *the difference in acidity or basicity of two solutions, and explain what the variable means.*

$$10^n$$ ◄──── where ___n___ is __the difference__ __between the two pH values__

🔑 **Characterize** indicators.

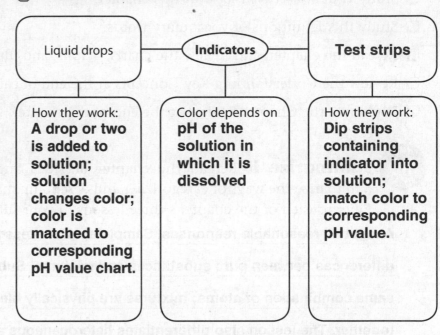

Liquid drops — Indicators — Test strips

| How they work: | Color depends on | How they work: |
| A drop or two is added to solution; solution changes color; color is matched to corresponding pH value chart. | pH of the solution in which it is dissolved | Dip strips containing indicator into solution; match color to corresponding pH value. |

🔑 **Compare and contrast** indicators *with* pH *meters.*

Method	Indicators	pH Meter
Accuracy	approximate	more accurate
How it works	Molecules change color.	Electrode senses hydronium ion concentration.

🔑 **Connect It** If you have heartburn, a condition of excess stomach acid, what food and drink might you want to avoid and why?

Accept all reasonable responses. Sample answer: Milk, tomatoes, citrus fruits and

foods containing vinegar are all acidic. They would add acid to the stomach and

could increase heartburn.

Mixtures, Solubility, and Acid/Base Solutions

Chapter Wrap-Up

Now that you have read the chapter, think about what you have learned.

Use this checklist to help you study.

❏ Complete your Foldables® Chapter Project.

❏ Study your *Science Notebook* on this chapter.

❏ Study the definitions of vocabulary words.

❏ Reread the chapter, and review the charts, graphs, and illustrations.

❏ Review the Understanding Key Concepts at the end of each lesson.

❏ Look over the Chapter Review at the end of the chapter.

 Summarize It Reread the chapter Big Idea and the lesson Key Concepts. Summarize the ways of categorizing and describing matter discussed in the chapter. Refer to each of the chapter's three lessons in your summary.

Accept all reasonable responses. Sample answer: Lesson 1 talks about the

differences between pure substances and mixtures. Substances are made of the

same combination of atoms; mixtures are physically blended but not bonded

together. The lesson also differentiates heterogeneous and homogeneous mixtures.

Heterogeneous mixtures are not evenly mixed; homogeneous mixtures are evenly

mixed and are also called solutions. Lesson 2 discusses the parts of solutions and

how solutions form. It differentiates the solvent, the substance with the greatest

volume in a solution, from solutes, the substances dissolved in the solvent. The

lesson also discusses how much solute is dissolved (concentration) and can be

dissolved (solubility) in a solvent. Lesson 3 distinguishes solutions by their pH

value. It differentiates between acid and base solutions and discusses their

properties and measurement.

Challenge *Keep a journal of matter that you encounter in a day. Make a chart that categorizes and describes the types of matter you encounter as elements, compounds, substances, mixtures, solutions, and so on. Present your chart of observations to your class.*

The Solar System

 What kinds of objects are in the solar system?

Before You Read

Before you read the chapter, think about what you know about the solar system. Record your thoughts in the first column. Pair with a partner, and discuss his or her thoughts. Write those thoughts in the second column. Record what you and your partner would like to share with the class in the third column.

Think	Pair	Share

Chapter

Lesson 1	Lesson 2	Lesson 3	Lesson 4
NEW asteroid comet astronomical unit period of revolution period of rotation **REVIEW** orbit	**NEW** terrestrial planet greenhouse effect	**NEW** Galilean moons	**NEW** meteoroid meteor meteorite impact crater

A Lesson Content Vocabulary page for each lesson is provided in the Chapter Resources Files.

> **Skim** *Lesson 1 in your book. Read the headings and look at the photos and illustrations. Identify three things you want to learn more about as you read the lesson. Record your ideas in your Science Journal.*

▪▪▪ **Main Idea** ▪▪▪	▪▪▪▪▪▪▪▪▪▪▪ **Details** ▪▪▪▪▪▪▪▪▪▪▪

What is the solar system?
I found this on page ___375___ .

Describe *the solar system.*

the Sun and the group of objects that move around it

Objects in the Solar System
I found this on page ___376___ .

Organize *facts about the Sun in this graphic organizer.*

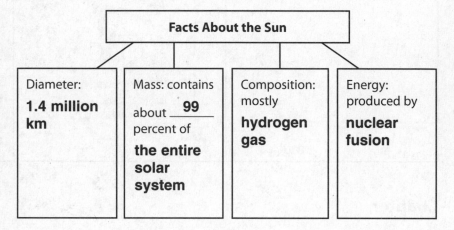

```
              Facts About the Sun

Diameter:     Mass: contains    Composition:    Energy:
              about  99         mostly          produced by
1.4 million   percent of                        nuclear
km            the entire        hydrogen        fusion
              solar            gas
              system
```

I found this on page ___376___ .

Explain *how an object is classified as a planet.*

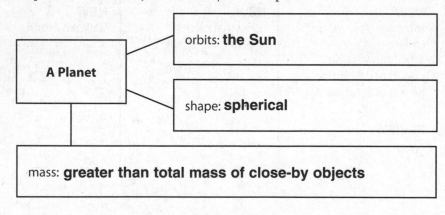

```
                    orbits: the Sun

A Planet
                    shape: spherical

      mass: greater than total mass of close-by objects
```

I found this on page ___377___ .

Identify *objects that orbit the Sun.*

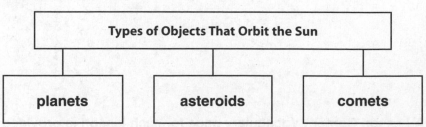

```
          Types of Objects That Orbit the Sun

   planets          asteroids          comets
```

Lesson 1 | The Structure of the Solar System (continued)

I found this on page _____377_____ .

🔑 **Contrast** *the inner and outer planets by completing the table.*

	Inner	**Outer**
Relative distance to the Sun	close	far away
Composition	solid, rocky materials	ice and gases
Relative size	small	large
Names of the planets	Mercury, Venus, Earth, Mars	Jupiter, Saturn, Uranus, Neptune

I found this on page _____377_____ .

Outline *information about dwarf planets,* asteroids, *and* comets. *Write three facts about each type of object.*

Other Objects in the Solar System

Dwarf Planets
1. orbit the Sun
2. not moons
3. located where there are many objects in nearby orbits

Asteroids
1. small and rocky
2. millions orbit between Mars and Jupiter
3. not spherical

Comets
1. made of gas, dust, and ice
2. have oval-shaped orbits
3. come from the outer parts of the solar system

I found this on page _____377_____ .

Identify *the names of four dwarf planets.*

1. **Ceres**
2. **Pluto**
3. **Eris**
4. **Makemake**

Main Idea

Details

I found this on page ___378___.

🔑 **Organize** *information about* astronomical units.

Definition: __the average distance from Earth to the Sun__

_____

Length: __about 150 million km__

Used because: __the distances between objects in the solar__

__system are so large__

The Motion of the Planets

I found this on page ___378___.

🔑 **Organize** *information about the motion of the planets by completing the chart.*

Motion of the Planets	
Rotation	**Revolution**
The time that a planet takes to __rotate once__ _____.	The time that a planet takes to **go** __around the Sun one time__ _____.
Also called: __spin__	Also called: __orbit__ Shape: __ellipse__

I found this on page ___379___.

Identify *the relationship between a planet's speed and its distance from the Sun by circling the correct speed.*

Distance from the Sun	Speed	
Closer to the Sun	(faster)	slower
Farther from the Sun	faster	(slower)

🔑 **Analyze It** Do Mercury and Venus travel through space faster than Earth? Are Mercury and Venus less than or greater than one AU from the Sun? Explain both answers.

__Accept all reasonable responses. Sample answer: Mercury and Venus travel faster than__

__Earth through space because they are closer to the Sun and are more affected by the__

__Sun's gravity. Both planets are less than one AU from the Sun, and Earth is one AU from__

__the Sun.__

Scan *Lesson 2 in your book. Think of three questions that you have about the inner planets. Write those questions in your Science Journal. Then try to answer them as you read.*

▪▪▪ **Main Idea** ▪▪▪

Planets Made of Rock
I found this on page _____383_____ .

▪▪▪▪▪ **Details** ▪▪▪▪▪

Model *the inner planets by drawing their orbits around the Sun. Color-code each planet and its orbit as follows: violet for Mercury, blue for Venus, green for Earth, and red for Mars.*
Students should draw four elliptical orbits around the Sun. The planets should be in this order from the Sun: Mercury, Venus, Earth, Mars.

I found this on page _____383_____ .

Describe *the inner planets by completing the diagram.*

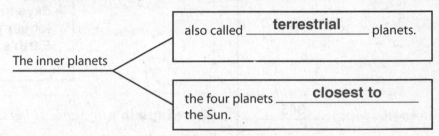

The inner planets

| also called ___**terrestrial**___ planets. |

| the four planets ___**closest to**___ the Sun. |

Mercury
I found this on page _____384_____ .

Organize *facts about Mercury by completing the spider map.*

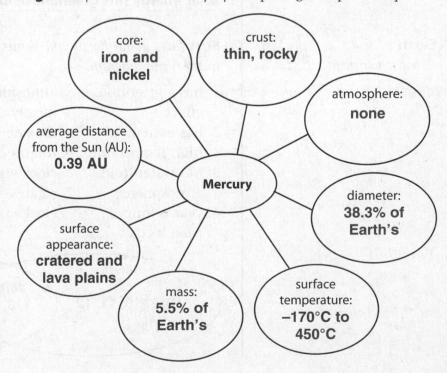

core:
iron and nickel

crust:
thin, rocky

atmosphere:
none

average distance
from the Sun (AU):
0.39 AU

Mercury

diameter:
38.3% of Earth's

surface
appearance:
cratered and lava plains

mass:
5.5% of Earth's

surface
temperature:
−170°C to 450°C

▪▪▪ Main Idea ▪▪▪

Venus
I found this on page ___385___ .

Sample answers are shown.

I found this on page ___385___ .

Earth
I found this on page ___386___ .

▪▪▪▪▪ Details ▪▪▪▪▪

🔑 **Compare and contrast** *characteristics of Mercury and Venus.*

Mercury
- no atmosphere
- **cratered surface**
- **much smaller than Earth**
- **day shorter than year**

Both
- inner planets
- **no moons**
- **closer to Sun than Earth**
- **have rocky surfaces**
- **years are shorter than Earth's**
- **days are much longer than Earth's.**

Venus
- thick atmosphere
- **surface covered with lava flows**
- **day longer than year**
- **almost the same size as Earth**

🔑 **Explain** *why Venus is hotter than Mercury.*

because the carbon dioxide in Venus's atmosphere traps

solar energy (the greenhouse effect)

Sort *facts about Earth and Venus. Place the number of each fact in the Venn diagram.*

1. has a greenhouse effect
2. has extremely high temperature
3. has water in its atmosphere
4. year is longer than its day
5. atmosphere mostly carbon dioxide
6. rotates counter-clockwise
7. rotates clockwise
8. a terrestrial planet
9. an inner planet
10. has a moon
11. has water on its surface
12. can support life

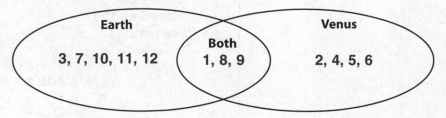

Earth
3, 7, 10, 11, 12

Both
1, 8, 9

Venus
2, 4, 5, 6

▪▪▪ **Main Idea** ▪▪▪ | ▪▪▪▪▪▪▪▪▪▪▪▪ **Details** ▪▪▪▪▪▪▪▪▪▪▪▪

Mars

I found this on page _____387_____.

Contrast *Earth and Mars. Circle the best answers.*

	Earth	**Mars**
Which phases of water are found there?	(ice) (liquid) (water vapor)	(ice) liquid water vapor
What is its distance to the Sun?	distance > 1 AU (distance = 1 AU) distance < 1 AU	(distance > 1 AU) distance = 1 AU distance < 1 AU
Describe the appearance of its surface.	Possible answer: broken into plates	Possible answer: covered with craters and lava flows
How many moons does it have?	(one) two	one (two)

I found this on page _____387_____.

🔑 **Summarize** *information about the inner planets. Place a check mark in each box that applies to each planet.*

	Mercury	**Venus**	**Earth**	**Mars**
Atmosphere		✓	✓	✓
Inner and outer core	✓	✓	✓	
Liquid outer core	✓	✓	✓	
Liquid core, only				✓
Solid inner core	✓	✓	✓	
Atmosphere 90% CO_2		✓		✓
Cratered surface	✓			✓
Liquid water on surface			✓	
Ice on surface			✓	✓
A moon or moons			✓	✓
Mantle and crust	✓	✓	✓	✓
Signs of volcanic action	✓	✓	✓	✓

🔑 **Synthesize It** From Earth, Venus looks like a very bright star in the night sky. If you could look at Earth from Venus, what would Earth look like? Explain your answer.

Accept all reasonable responses. Sample answer: Earth would look like a bright star

too, but it might look dimmer because it is farther from the Sun than Venus is.

> **Predict** *three things that will be discussed in Lesson 3. Read the headings and look at the photos and illustrations. Write your predictions in your Science Journal.*

■ ■ ■ **Main Idea** ■ ■ ■ | ■ ■ ■ ■ ■ ■ **Details** ■ ■ ■ ■ ■ ■

The Gas Giants
I found this on page _____391_____ .

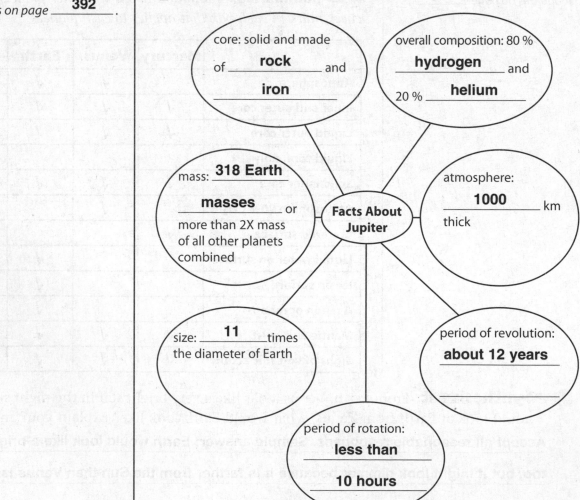 **Detail** *three ways in which the outer planets are similar*

1. Composed of: __hydrogen and helium__

2. Gravitational force: __very strong__

3. Structure: __thick gas and liquid layers covering a small__ __solid core__

Jupiter
I found this on page _____392_____ .

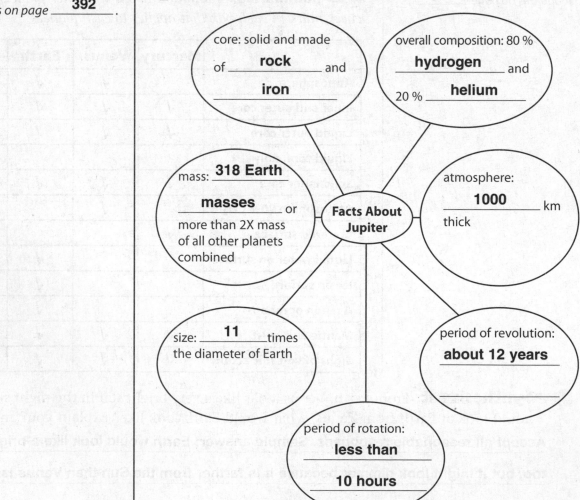 **Describe** *Jupiter by completing the spider map.*

core: solid and made of _____**rock**_____ and _____**iron**_____

overall composition: 80 % _____**hydrogen**_____ and 20 % _____**helium**_____

mass: __318 Earth__ __masses_____ or more than 2X mass of all other planets combined

Facts About Jupiter

atmosphere: _____**1000**_____ km thick

size: _____**11**_____ times the diameter of Earth

period of revolution: __about 12 years__

period of rotation: __less than__ __10 hours__

■■■ **Main Idea** ■■■ | ■■■■■■■■■■■ **Details** ■■■■■■■■■■■

I found this on page ___392___ .

Identify *Jupiter's* Galilean moons.

1. Io

2. Europa

3. Ganymede

4. Callisto

I found this on page ___393___ .

Relate *Jupiter's moons to the formation of the planet's rings.*

Collisions between Jupiter's moons and meteorites likely

resulted in the particles that make up the planet's rings.

Saturn
I found this on page ___393___ .

🔑 **Compare and contrast** *Saturn and Jupiter in the chart below.*

Saturn	Jupiter
Different	Different

Saturn (Different)	Same	Jupiter (Different)
ring system: **large, complex**	atmosphere: hydrogen and helium	ring system: **faint**
diameter: ___9.4___ times Earth's diameter	core: solid	diameter: ___11.2___ times Earth's diameter
average distance from Sun: ___9.6___ AU	rings	average distance from Sun: ___5.2___ AU
appearance of atmosphere: colorful **bands**	many moons	appearance of atmosphere: colorful **bands** and Great **Red Spot**

▪▪▪ **Main Idea** ▪▪▪ | ▪▪▪▪▪▪▪▪▪▪▪▪▪▪ **Details** ▪▪▪▪▪▪▪▪▪▪▪▪

Uranus and Neptune
I found this on page ___394___ .

Sample answers are shown.

🔑 **Compare and contrast** *characteristics of Uranus and Neptune. Include at least ten facts in your response.*

Uranus	**Both**	**Neptune**
• has at least 27 moons, all of which are smaller than Earth's moon	• outer planets • gas giant	• at least 13 moons
	• diameter about 4X that of Earth	• 30.1 AU from the Sun
• axis of rotation tilted on side	• faint ring systems	
	• atmosphere of hydrogen and helium with some methane	• largest moon called Triton
• 19.2 AU from the Sun		
	• rock and iron core	
	• explored by *Voyager II* space probe	

I found this on page ___395___ .

🔑 **Identify** *four characteristics common to all the outer planets.* **Sample answers are shown.**

1. rings _____

2. made mostly of hydrogen and helium _____

3. large _____

4. several moons _____

🔑 **Connect It** Hydrogen, helium, and methane are gases on Earth. Why are these substances liquids on the gas giants?

Accept all reasonable responses. Sample answer: For a gas to become a liquid, it must

be exposed to low temperature and/or high pressure. Both of those conditions exist on

the gas giants. These planets are cold because they are so far from the Sun, and

pressure is high because the gas giants are so massive.

Skim *Lesson 4 in your book. Read the headings and look at the photos and illustrations. Identify three things that you want to learn about as you read the lesson. Record your ideas in your Science Journal.*

▪▪▪ Main Idea ▪▪▪

Dwarf Planets

I found this on page **399** .

▪▪▪▪▪ Details ▪▪▪▪▪

🔑 **Compare and contrast** *a planet and a dwarf planet in the Venn diagram below.*

Planet

Both

Dwarf Planet

Sample answer: mass is greater than total mass of all other objects whose orbits are close by

spherical shape; orbits a star

objects of similar mass orbit nearby or cross its orbital path

I found this on page **400** .

Organize *information about dwarf planets.*

Dwarf Planets			
	Pluto	**Ceres**	**Eris**
Location in solar system	outside orbit of Neptune	in the asteroid belt	3X farther from the Sun than Pluto
Composition	rocky core surrounded by ice	rocky core surrounded by ice	probably like Pluto
Number of moons	3	none known	1

I found this on page **400** .

Describe *Makemake and Haumea.*

Both are dwarf plants that are smaller than Pluto and found

in the Kuiper belt.

<table>
<tr><th>■■■ **Main Idea** ■■■</th><th>■■■■■■■ **Details** ■■■■■■■</th></tr>
</table>

Main Idea	Details

Asteroids

I found this on page __401__ .

Relate *facts about asteroids in the table below*

Facts About Asteroids	
Location	mostly in the asteroid belt, between Mars and Jupiter
Number	hundreds of thousands
Description	chunks of rock and ice that never clumped together to form a planet
Largest (name and size)	Pallas; 500 km in diameter

Comets

I found this on page __401__ .

🔑 **Compare and Contrast** *asteroids and comets by completing the chart.*

Asteroids and Comets	
Same	**Different**
• Both orbit the Sun.	• Comets have tails; asteroids do not.
• Both are made of rock, ice and dust.	• Comets have greatly elongated orbits; most asteroids orbit the Sun in the asteroid belt.

I found this on page __401__ .

Model *the structure of comets by adding two comets to the figure below. Draw one comet approaching the Sun and one comet going away from the Sun. Indicate the direction of motion with arrows. Show the comets' comas and dust tails.*

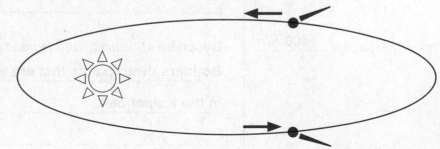

Lesson 4 | Dwarf Planets and Other Objects (continued)

▪▪▪ Main Idea ▪▪▪

I found this on page ___402___.

▪▪▪▪▪▪▪▪▪▪▪ Details ▪▪▪▪▪▪▪▪▪▪▪

Distinguish *information about the source of comets below.*

The Kuiper Belt is **the source of short-period comets.**

The Oort Cloud is **the source of long-period comets.**

Meteoroids

I found this on page ___402___.

Sample answers are shown.

Analyze *the differences between a* meteoroid, *a* meteor, *and a* meteorite *by completing the chart.*

Name of Body	What It Is
Meteoroid	a small, rocky particle that moves through space
Meteor	a streak of light in the sky, made by a meteoroid falling through Earth's atmosphere
Meteorite	a meteoroid that strikes a planet or a moon

🗝️ **Describe** *an* impact crater *and how one is formed.*

a round depression formed on the surface of a planet,

moon, or other space object by the impact of a meteorite

🗝️ **Analyze It** Which attribute is more important in classifying a solar system object, its size or its composition? Explain.

Sample answer: Most objects in the solar system are made of similar materials, such

as gases, rocks, and ice. Therefore, classification is determined more by size than by

composition.

Chapter Wrap-Up

Now that you have read the chapter, think about what you have learned.

Use this checklist to help you study.

❏ Complete your Foldables® Chapter Project.

❏ Study your *Science Notebook* on this chapter.

❏ Study the definitions of vocabulary words.

❏ Reread the chapter, and review the charts, graphs, and illustrations.

❏ Review the Understanding Key Concepts at the end of each lesson.

❏ Look over the Chapter Review at the end of the chapter.

THE BIG IDEA

Summarize It Reread the chapter Big Idea and the lesson Key Concepts. As telescopes and methods of observing space have improved over time, scientists have discovered evidence of planets revolving around other stars. In addition to planets, what other objects would you expect to find in those distant solar systems? What might the orbits of objects in those solar systems look like?

Accept all reasonable responses. Sample answer: Rocky planets, gas giants,

comets, asteroids, and dwarf planets might revolve around those stars. The planets

would probably have elliptical orbits. The comets would have elongated orbits that

could take them far from the star and then back again, at which point they would

develop tails.

_____

_____

_____

_____

_____

_____

Challenge *Jupiter is an enormous planet with nearly the same composition as the Sun. What if Jupiter were a star instead of a planet, giving our solar system two suns? How might that circumstance affect Jupiter's moons? How might it affect Earth and the rest of the solar system?*

Stars and Galaxies

What makes up the universe, and how does gravity affect the universe?

Before You Read

Before you read the chapter, think about what you know about stars and galaxies. Record three things that you already know about the universe in the first column. Then write three things that you would like to learn about the universe in the second column. Complete the final column of the chart when you have finished this chapter.

| K
What I Know | W
What I Want to Learn | L
What I Learned |
|---|---|---|
| | | |

Chapter Vocabulary

Lesson 1	Lesson 2	Lesson 3	Lesson 4
NEW
spectroscope
astronomical unit
light-year
apparent magnitude
luminosity

ACADEMIC
apparent | **NEW**
nuclear fusion
star
radiative zone
convection zone
photosphere
chromosphere
corona
Hertzsprung-Russell
   diagram | **NEW**
nebula
white dwarf
supernova
neutron star
black hole

REVIEW
neutron | **NEW**
galaxy
dark matter
Big Bang theory
Doppler shift |

A Lesson Content Vocabulary page for each lesson is provided in the Chapter Resources Files.

Scan *Lesson 1. Read the lesson titles and bold words. Look at the pictures. Identify three facts you discovered about how astronomers observe the night sky. Record your facts in your Science Journal.*

▪▪▪ **Main Idea** ▪▪▪

Looking at the Night Sky
I found this on page ___415___ .

I found this on page ___416___ .

I found this on page ___416___ .

▪▪▪ **Details** ▪▪▪

Explain *facts associated with viewing the night sky.*

Few people see a night sky very full of stars.

↓

City lights make many stars too faint to be seen.

Objects in the night sky appear to move.

↓

Earth rotates on its axis once every 24 hours.

Characterize *astronomy before the invention of the telescope.*

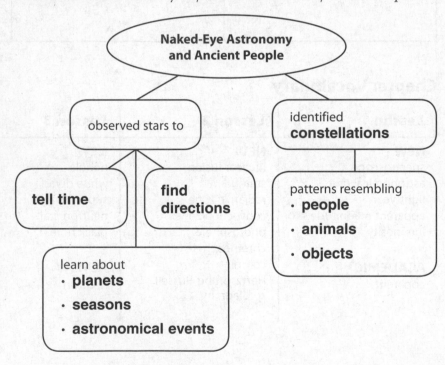

Naked-Eye Astronomy and Ancient People

observed stars to

- **tell time**
- **find directions**

learn about
- **planets**
- **seasons**
- **astronomical events**

identified **constellations**

patterns resembling
- **people**
- **animals**
- **objects**

🔑 **Assess** *the usefulness of constellations to astronomers.*

Sample answer: Dividing the sky into patterns and regions

helps astronomers communicate to others what area of the

sky they are studying.

Lesson 1 | The View from Earth (continued)

▪▪▪ Main Idea ▪▪▪

I found this on page **417**.

lowest

↓

highest ▼

I found this on page **417**.

I found this on page **417**.

▪▪▪ Details ▪▪▪

🔑 **Categorize** *observations that astronomers can study at various wavelengths.*

Waves	Used to study
Radio	**cold, dark regions of space**
Infrared	**star-forming regions**
Ultraviolet	**young stars**
X-rays and gamma rays	**high-energy gas jets**

Draw *an arrow beside the table above to show the energy level of wavelengths in the direction of lowest energy to highest energy.*

🔑 **Identify** *three characteristics of stars that astronomers can study using spectroscopes.*

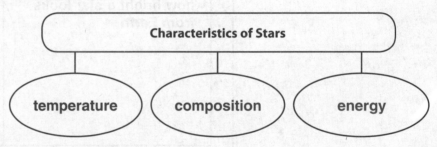

Characteristics of Stars

temperature — composition — energy

Measuring Distances

I found this on page **418**.

Contrast *terms associated with measuring distance in the universe.*

Parallax	Astronomical unit	Light-year
the apparent change in an object's position caused by looking at it from two different points	**the average distance between Earth and the Sun**	**the distance light travels in one year**
	about **150 million** km	about **10 trillion** km

••• Main Idea ••• | ••••••• Details •••••••

Measuring Brightness
I found this on page ___419___ .

🔑 **Identify** *two ways astronomers measure the brightness of stars.*

1. **by how bright they appear from Earth** _____

2. **by how bright they actually are** _____

I found this on page ___419___ .

Relate *the appearance of celestial objects with the number values of their* apparent magnitudes.

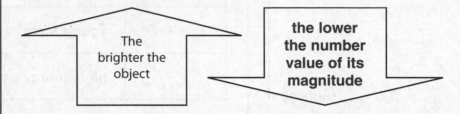

The brighter the object → the lower the number value of its magnitude

I found this on page ___419___ .

🔑 **Contrast** apparent magnitude *and* absolute magnitude. *Circle the magnitude that measures* luminosity.

Apparent Magnitude	Absolute Magnitude
how bright a star looks from Earth	how bright the star actually is, based on its temperature and size, regardless of its distance and appearance from Earth

I found this on page ___419___ .

Answers can appear in any order.

🔑 **Complete** *the statement below.*

If a scientist knows a star's ____luminosity____ and its

____apparent magnitude____, he or she can calculate

the star's ____distance____.

🔑 **Analyze It** Explain why it is not possible to know what is going on elsewhere in the universe at exactly this moment.

Accept all reasonable responses. Sample answer: It takes time for light to travel

(including both visible light and other electromagnetic wavelengths). By the time any

observable waves from stars reach Earth, we are seeing what those stars looked like

anywhere from a few years ago to millions of years ago.

Predict *three facts that will be discussed in Lesson 2 after reading the headings. Record your predictions in your Science Journal.*

=== **Main Idea** === | ============= **Details** ==============

How Stars Shine
I found this on page ___423___ .

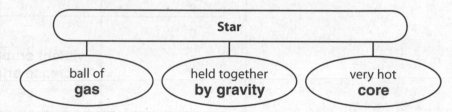 **Sequence** *the process of* nuclear fusion.

1. Atoms of hot gas move quickly.
2. Atoms _____collide_____, and nuclei _____stick together_____.
3. Great amounts of _____energy_____ are released, making the star shine.

I found this on page ___423___ .

Characterize *a* star.

Star
- ball of **gas**
- held together **by gravity**
- very hot **core**

Composition and Structure of Stars
I found this on page ___423___ .

Explain *why the Sun is the most easily observed* star.

It is close to Earth. Scientists can send probes to study the

Sun and can observe it with Earth-based spectroscopes.

I found this on page ___424___ .

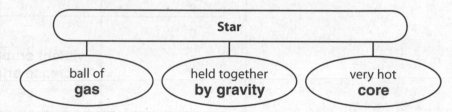 **Describe** *the inner and outer layers of the Sun.*

	Layer	Description
Interior Layers	Core	inner-most layer where hydrogen is fused into helium
	Radiative zone	a shell of cooler hydrogen above the core
	Convection zone	hot gas moves toward the surface and cooler gas moves deeper into the interior
Outer Layers	Photosphere	the apparent surface of the star
	Chromosphere	the orange-red layer above the photosphere
	Corona	the wide, outermost layer of the star's atmosphere

▪▪▪ Main Idea ▪▪▪

I found this on page __425__ .

▪▪▪▪▪▪ Details ▪▪▪▪▪▪

🗝️ **Detail** *features that change on the Sun over short periods of time.*

Feature	Details
Sunspots	**regions of strong magnetic activity that are cooler than the rest of the photosphere**
Prominences	**clouds of gas that make loops and jets extending into the corona**
Flares	**violent eruptions that suddenly increase brightness**
Coronal Mass Ejections (CMEs)	**huge bubbles of gas ejected from the corona**
Solar wind	**charged particles that stream continually away from the Sun**

Groups of Stars

I found this on page __426__ .

Categorize *ways* stars *exist in space.*

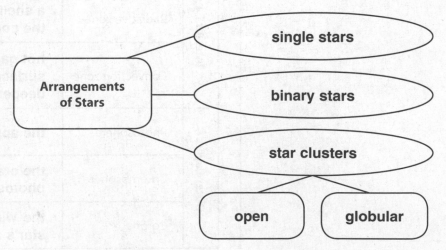

Lesson 2 | The Sun and Other Stars (continued)

▪▪▪ **Main Idea** ▪▪▪ | ▪▪▪▪▪▪▪▪▪▪▪ **Details** ▪▪▪▪▪▪▪▪▪▪▪

Classifying Stars
I found this on page _____426_____ .

🔑 **Order** stars' *colors, generally, by temperature. Draw arrows to represent increasing mass.*

Color	Temperature	Mass
Blue-white	↑	↑
White	↑	↑
Yellow	↑	↑
Orange	↑	↑
Red	↑	↑

I found this on page _____427_____ .

🔑 **Characterize** the Hertzsprung-Russell diagram.

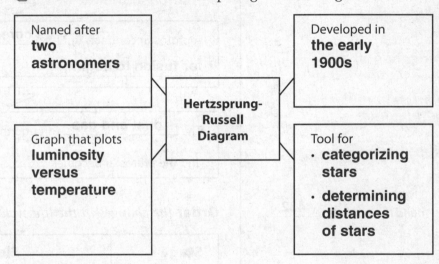

Named after **two astronomers**

Developed in **the early 1900s**

Hertzsprung-Russell Diagram

Graph that plots **luminosity versus temperature**

Tool for
• **categorizing stars**
• **determining distances of stars**

I found this on page _____427_____ .

Generalize *trends on the main sequence of the* Hertzsprung-Russell diagram.

Mass, temperature, and luminosity decrease in a line drawn

from upper left to lower right.

🔑 **Synthesize It** Compare and contrast the Sun with other stars in the universe.

Accept all reasonable responses. Sample answer: The Sun, like all other stars, is

composed of layers, is undergoing a process of nuclear fusion, and is radiating

energy. It is a singular star that does not exist in a pair or cluster. The Sun is small

compared with a blue-white giant, but scientists suspect the Sun is bigger than 90%

of other stars.

Evolution of Stars

> **Skim** *Lesson 3 in your book. Read the headings and look at the photos and illustrations. Identify three things you want to learn more about as you read the lesson. Record your ideas in your Science Journal.*

■■■ **Main Idea** ■■■ | ■■■■■■■■ **Details** ■■■■■■■■

Life Cycle of a Star
I found this on page ___431___ .

🔑 **Sequence** *the change of a* nebula *to a visible star.*

A nebula begins as a ___**cold**___ , ___**dense**___ , and ___**dark**___ cloud of ___**gas**___ and ___**dust**___ .

⬇

___**Gravity**___ causes the ___**densest**___ parts to ___**collapse**___ forming ___**protostars**___ .

⬇

A protostar contracts until **its core is hot and dense enough for fusion to begin** .

⬇

The ___**dust and gas**___ around the protostar ___**blow away**___ , and the protostar becomes ___**a visible star**___ .

I found this on page ___432___ .

Order *the changes in the life cycle of a massive star.*

Stage	Elements Formed
Massive star and red giant	• hydrogen → **helium** • helium → **carbon**
Larger red giant	• hydrogen → **helium** • helium → **carbon** • carbon → **other elements**
Red supergiant	hydrogen → helium → ___**carbon**___ → ___**neon**___ → ___**oxygen**___ → ___**silicon**___ → ___**iron**___

End of a Star
I found this on page ___433___ .

🔑 **Explain** *why the Sun will not become a supergiant. Identify what it will become.*

The Sun does not have enough mass to fuse elements beyond helium. The Sun's core will become a white dwarf.

Lesson 3 | Evolution of Stars (continued)

• • • Main Idea • • • | **• • • • • • • • Details • • • • • • • •**

I found this on page ___433___ .

Sequence *what will happen to the solar system when the Sun runs out of fuel.*

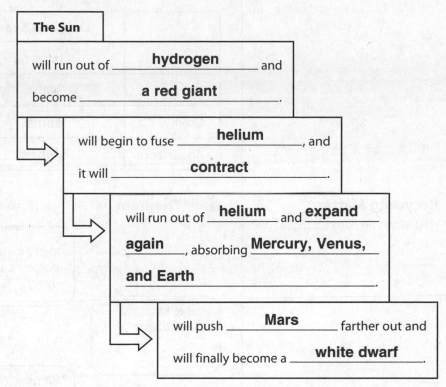

The Sun

will run out of ___**hydrogen**___ and become ___**a red giant**___.

will begin to fuse ___**helium**___, and it will ___**contract**___.

will run out of ___**helium**___ and ___**expand**___ ___**again**___, absorbing ___**Mercury, Venus, and Earth**___.

will push ___**Mars**___ farther out and will finally become a ___**white dwarf**___.

I found this on page ___433___ .

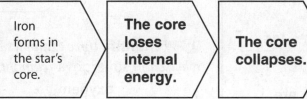

Order *the formation of a* supernova.

| Iron forms in the star's core. | The core loses internal energy. | The core collapses. | The star explodes. |

I found this on page ___434___ .

Characterize neutron stars.

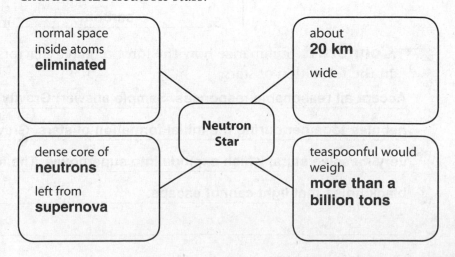

normal space inside atoms **eliminated**

about **20 km** wide

Neutron Star

dense core of **neutrons** left from **supernova**

teaspoonful would weigh **more than a billion tons**

■■■ **Main Idea** ■■■   ■■■■■■■■■■ **Details** ■■■■■■■■■■

I found this on page _____434_____ .

Compare and contrast *a* black hole *with the star from which it formed.*

	Original Star	Black Hole
Size	larger	smaller
Mass	same	same
Gravity	same	same
Appearance	shines	not visible

Recycling Matter

I found this on page _____435_____ .

🔑 **Diagram** *the cycle of a planetary* nebula.

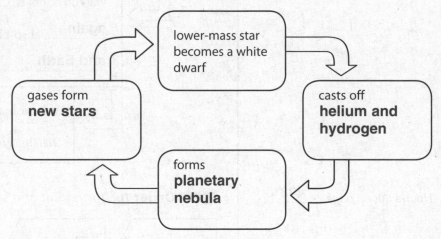

lower-mass star becomes a white dwarf

casts off **helium and hydrogen**

forms **planetary nebula**

gases form **new stars**

I found this on page _____435_____ .

🔑 **Identify** *three examples of elements found on Earth that are released in* supernova *remnants.*

1. _____oxygen_____ in _____air_____

2. _____silicon_____ in _____rocks_____

3. _____carbon_____ in _____all life forms_____

Sample answers are shown.

🔑 **Connect It** Summarize how the force of gravity factors into at least three processes in the formation of stars.

Accept all reasonable responses. Sample answer: Gravity pulls dust and gas in

nebulae together during the initial formation of stars. Gravity collapses the core of

very massive stars, which explode into supernovae. The force of gravity is so great in

black holes that light cannot escape.

> **Predict** *three facts that will be discussed in Lesson 4 after reading the headings. Record your predictions in your Science Journal.*

■ ■ ■ **Main Idea** ■ ■ ■

Galaxies
I found this on page ___439___ .

I found this on page ___439___ .

I found this on page ___440___ .

Sample answers are shown.

■ ■ ■ ■ ■ ■ **Details** ■ ■ ■ ■ ■ ■

Relate *the number of stars in galaxies and the universe.*

Galaxy	Universe
hundreds of billions of **stars**	hundreds of billions of **galaxies**

Contrast *scientific knowledge about dark matter.*

Dark Matter	
Scientists know that…	**it emits no light at any wavelength.**
Scientists hypothesize that…	**it makes up more than 90 percent of the universe's mass.**
Scientists don't know…	**what material it contains.**

🔑 **Categorize** *details about types of galaxies. List at least four details about each type.*

Spiral	Elliptical	Irregular
· spiral arms	· no internal structure	· oddly shaped
· central disk	· sphere or football shape	· many young stars
· thicker central bulge	· higher percentage of old, red stars	· areas of intense star formation
· globular clusters and older, redder stars around disk	· little or no gas or dust	· form from gravity of neighbor galaxies

▪▪▪ **Main Idea** ▪▪▪ | ▪▪▪▪▪▪▪▪▪▪▪▪▪▪ **Details** ▪▪▪▪▪▪▪▪▪▪▪

I found this on page ___441___ .

Explain *why scientists liken the large-scale structure of the universe to a sponge.*

They compare it to a sponge because galaxies are

clustered together around regions of nearly empty space.

_____

The Milky Way

I found this on page ___441___ .

🔑 **Characterize** *the Milky Way.*

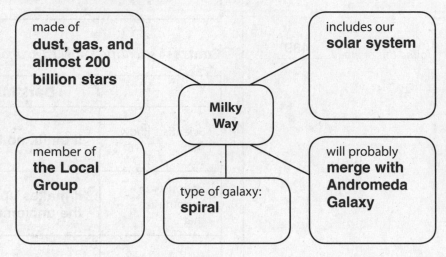

made of **dust, gas, and almost 200 billion stars**

includes our **solar system**

Milky Way

member of **the Local Group**

type of galaxy: **spiral**

will probably **merge with Andromeda Galaxy**

I found this on page ___442___ .

Illustrate *the Milky Way, and describe Earth's position in it.*

Student drawings should feature the football-shaped disk in the center, the two large spiral arms projecting from the ends of the disk, and the less defined arms spiraling between the larger ones.

Earth's position: _____ **inside the disk** _____

The Big Bang Theory

I found this on page ___444___ .

🔑 **Restate** *the Big Bang theory.*

The universe began from one point billions of years ago

and has been expanding ever since.

_____

Main Idea

Details

I found this on page __444__ .

🔑 **Sequence** *the expansion of the universe.*

| 13 to 14 billion years ago, the universe was dense and hot. | → | It cooled for **a few hundred thousand years** | → | **Atoms** formed. | → |

| **Stars** formed. | → | Gravity pulled **stars into galaxies** | → | Galaxies move farther apart as the universe expands. |

I found this on page __444__ .

Differentiate *sound waves in the* Doppler shift.

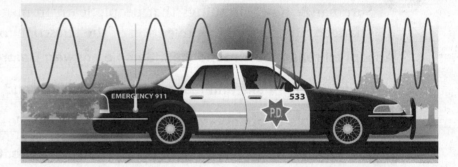

To an observer in front of the car's motion:
Sound waves compress as the car moves forward.

To an observer behind the car:
Sound waves spread out as the car moves away.

I found this on page __444__ .

Relate *dark energy to the rate the universe is expanding.*

Scientists theorize that dark energy is pushing galaxies apart because __galaxies are moving apart faster over time__ .

🔑 **Synthesize It** Predict what will happen to the Sun, the solar system, and the Milky Way in billions of years.

Accept all reasonable responses. Sample answer: The Sun will have long since

become a white dwarf. Most of the matter in the solar system will probably have been

recycled into other stars. The Milky Way will merge with other galaxies and be pushed

farther from the center of the universe.

Stars and Galaxies

Chapter Wrap-Up

Now that you have read the chapter, think about what you have learned. Complete the final column in the chart on the first page of the chapter.

Use this checklist to help you study.

❏ Complete your Foldables® Chapter Project.

❏ Study your *Science Notebook* on this chapter.

❏ Study the definitions of vocabulary words.

❏ Reread the chapter, and review the charts, graphs, and illustrations.

❏ Review the Understanding Key Concepts at the end of each lesson.

❏ Look over the Chapter Review at the end of the chapter.

THE BIG IDEA **Summarize It** Reread the chapter Big Idea and the lesson Key Concepts. Summarize how the things that people learn from looking at the night sky have changed from before the invention of the telescope to the present.

Accept all reasonable responses. Sample answer: Before the telescope, people

watched the night sky and learned to measure time and seasons and to navigate.

When the tools of observation improved to include telescopes and spectroscopes,

people learned much more about the numbers of stars, their composition, how they

are grouped, and their distances from each other in the universe. Understanding

how stars are made and what they are made of helps us know about all matter,

including what we ourselves are made of.

_____

_____

_____

_____

_____

Challenge *Do more research about the Big Bang theory. Find out the most current hypotheses that scientists have about what might have caused it and what happened* before *the Big Bang.*

Name _____   Date _____

Minerals and Rocks

 How are minerals and rocks formed, identified, classified, and used?

Before You Read

Before you read the chapter, think about what you know about minerals and rocks. Record your ideas in the first column. Pair with a partner, and discuss his or her thoughts. Write those ideas in the second column. Then record what you both would like to share with the class in the third column.

Think	Pair	Share

Chapter Vocabulary

Lesson 1	Lesson 2	Lesson 3
NEW	**NEW**	**NEW**
mineral	rock	rock cycle
crystal structure	grain	extrusive rock
crystallization	magma	intrusive rock
streak	lava	uplift
luster	texture	deposition
cleavage	sediment	
fracture	lithification	
ore	foliation	
ACADEMIC		
exhibit		

A Lesson Content Vocabulary page for each lesson is provided in the Chapter Resources Files.

Lesson 1 Minerals

Predict *three facts that will be discussed in Lesson 1 after reading the headings. Record your predictions in your Science Journal.*

■■■ **Main Idea** ■■■

What is a mineral?
I found this on page _____ 461 ____ .

I found this on page _____ 462 ____ .

I found this on page _____ 463 ____ .

■■■ **Details** ■■■

Identify *the 5 characteristics that define a* mineral.

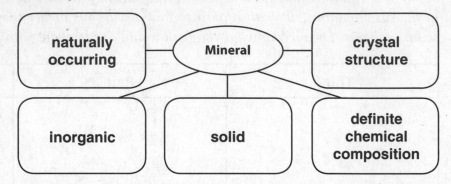

Paraphrase *the meanings of* crystal structure *and definite chemical composition as they relate to* minerals.

Crystal Structure	**Definite Chemical Composition**
The atoms in a mineral are arranged in an orderly, repeating pattern that forms the smooth faces and sharp edges of a crystal.	A mineral is made of specific amounts of elements, represented by a chemical formula.

🗝 **Compare and contrast** crystallization *from magma with* crystallization *from water.*

In the case of crystallization from magma, atoms form crystals as molten rock material cools;

Both occur when a liquid cools and atoms within the liquid form a solid with an orderly, repeating pattern.

in the case of crystallization from water, the particles of a dissolved substance join as the water evaporates.

■■■ Main Idea ■■■ | **■■■■■■ Details ■■■■■■**

Mineral Identification

🗝 **Differentiate** *properties used to identify* minerals.

Property	Description
Density	One mineral sample feels heavier than another sample of the same size because it has more mass in the same volume.
Hardness	**the observation of how easily a mineral is scratched or how easily it scratches something else** Ranked how? **the Mohs hardness scale**
Color	**the observable color of the surface of a mineral; can vary from specimen to specimen**
Streak	the color of a mineral's powder How does it differ from color? **It does not vary from specimen to specimen.**
Luster	**the way a mineral's surface reflects light** Terms: **metallic, glassy, earthy, pearly**
Cleavage	**the tendency to break along a smooth, flat surface**
Fracture	**the tendency to break along rough or irregular surfaces**
Crystal shape	determined by a mineral's atomic structure Examples: **massive, six-sided, pyramid**

I found this on page ___464___ .

I found this on page ___464___ .

I found this on page ___465___ .

I found this on page ___465___ .

I found this on page ___465___ .

I found this on page ___465___ .

I found this on page ___465___ .

I found this on page ___466___ .

Lesson 1 | Minerals (continued)

... **Main Idea** ... | ... **Details** ...

I found this on page ___466___ .

Exemplify *six unusual* mineral *properties.*

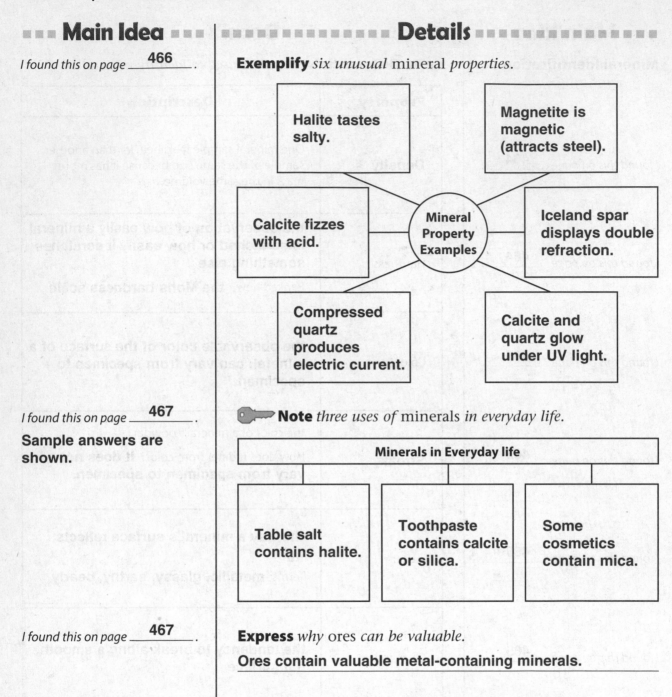

Halite tastes salty.

Magnetite is magnetic (attracts steel).

Calcite fizzes with acid.

Mineral Property Examples

Iceland spar displays double refraction.

Compressed quartz produces electric current.

Calcite and quartz glow under UV light.

I found this on page ___467___ .

Sample answers are shown.

Note *three uses of* minerals *in everyday life.*

Minerals in Everyday life

Table salt contains halite.

Toothpaste contains calcite or silica.

Some cosmetics contain mica.

I found this on page ___467___ .

Express *why* ores *can be valuable.*

Ores contain valuable metal-containing minerals.

Analyze It Suppose you find a mineral that you have never seen before. Why must you evaluate several of the mineral's properties in order to identify it? Is there a way to identify a mineral by observing just one property?

Accept all reasonable responses. Sample answer: Most minerals share properties

with other minerals, so it is necessary to look at several properties in order to identify

a mineral with certainty. The exception would be if you could identify the mineral's

chemical composition because its chemical formula is unique.

Skim *Lesson 2 in your book. Read the headings and look at the photos and illustrations. Identify three things you want to learn more about rocks as you read the lesson. Record your ideas in your Science Journal.*

▪▪▪ **Main Idea** ▪▪▪ | ▪▪▪▪▪▪▪▪ **Details** ▪▪▪▪▪▪▪▪

What is a rock?
I found this on page ___**471**___.

Organize *characteristics of* rocks.

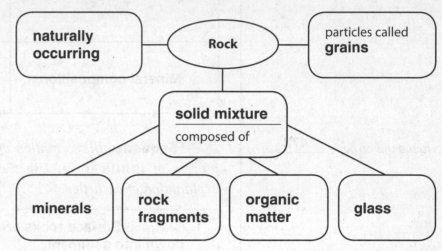

Classifying Rocks
I found this on page ___**472**___.

Identify *the 3 major types of* rocks.

1. __igneous_____

2. __metamorphic_____

3. __sedimentary_____

I found this on page ___**472**___.

Compare and contrast magma *and* lava.

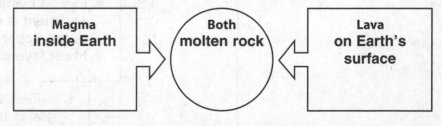

I found this on page ___**472**___.

Relate *the formation of igneous* rock.

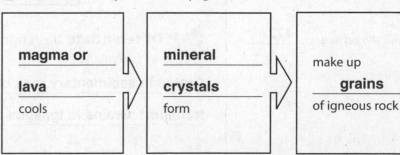

Minerals and Rocks **135**

▪▪▪ Main Idea ▪▪▪

▪▪▪▪▪▪▪ Details ▪▪▪▪▪▪▪▪

I found this on page ___472___ .

🔑 **Describe** two characteristics geologists use to classify igneous rock.

Characteristic	Description
Texture	the size of grains and how they are arranged
Mineral composition	what minerals the rock contains

I found this on page ___473___ .

🔑 **Sequence** the formation of sedimentary rock through the process of lithification. Use the term in parentheses in your explanation of each step.

1. (sediment) **Surface rocks are broken down into sediment.**

2. (erosion) **Erosion transports sediment grains.**

3. (basins) **Sediment is deposited in low areas called basins.**

4. (layers) **Layers build up as more sediment is deposited. The weight of the upper layers compacts the lower layers.**

5. (cement) **Dissolved solids cement the grains together into sedimentary rock.**

I found this on page ___473___ .

🔑 **Differentiate** the grains of sedimentary rock from the grains of igneous rock.

Grains in sedimentary rock often become rounded during

transport. Grains in igneous rocks are usually sharp.

Lesson 2 | Rocks (continued)

⫶⫶⫶ **Main Idea** ⫶⫶⫶ | ⫶⫶⫶⫶⫶⫶⫶⫶⫶⫶ **Details** ⫶⫶⫶⫶⫶⫶⫶⫶⫶⫶

I found this on page ___474___ .

🔑 **Explain** *the process of metamorphism.*

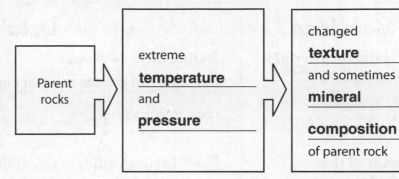

I found this on page ___475___ .

Describe foliation, *and contrast the appearance of bands in foliated and nonfoliated metamorphic rocks.*

Foliation: **a layered appearance that forms when uneven pressures cause flat minerals to line up**

Foliated	Nonfoliated
bands of light and dark minerals	no bands

Rocks in Everyday Life
I found this on page ___475___ .

🔑 **Relate** *properties of* rocks *to examples of their uses.*

Rock	Property	Use
Granite	strong and beautiful	fountains
Pumice	hard and abrasive	polishing and cleansing products
Sandstone	natural layering	building materials
Slate	foliation; splits into flat pieces	shingles

🔑 **Synthesize It** Briefly summarize the ways the three major rock types form.

Accept all reasonable responses. Sample answer: Igneous rocks crystallize as molten rock cools. Sedimentary rocks form when grains of sediment are cemented together or when crystals form as water evaporates. Metamorphic rocks form when high temperature and pressure change parent rocks without erosion or melting.

Predict *three facts that will be discussed in Lesson 3 after reading the headings. Record your predictions about the rock cycle in your Science Journal.*

▪▪▪ **Main Idea** ▪▪▪ | ━━ 🔑 **Details** ▪▪▪▪▪▪▪▪▪▪▪▪▪▪▪▪

What is the rock cycle?

I found this on page ___479___ .

Define *the* rock cycle.

the series of processes that continually change one type of

rock into another

Processes of the Rock Cycle

🔑 **Distinguish** *processes of the* rock cycle. *Write an S below processes that can occur on Earth's surface.*

I found this on page ___480___ .

I found this on page ___480___ .

I found this on page ___481___ .

I found this on page ___481___ .

I found this on page ___481___ .

I found this on page ___481___ .

I found this on page ___481___ .

I found this on page ___480___ .

Processes	Description
Cooling and crystallization S	Melted rock material either erupts and cools at Earth's surface or solidifies below the surface.
Uplift	Tectonic activity moves rock upward to the surface from below.
Weathering S	Glaciers, wind, and rain break down rock.
Erosion S	Glaciers, wind, and rain carry sediment to low-lying locations.
Deposition S	Sediment settles in a new location in layers.
Compaction	Weight of overlying layers of sediment presses down on lower layers.
Cementation	Dissolved minerals crystallize and cement grains of sediment together.

🔑 **Differentiate** intrusive rock *and* extrusive rock.

Intrusive	Extrusive
forms when magma cools and crystallizes below Earth's surface	forms when lava erupts, cools, and crystallizes on Earth's surface

▪▪▪ **Main Idea** ▪▪▪ | ▪▪▪▪▪▪▪▪▪▪▪▪ **Details** ▪▪▪▪▪▪▪▪▪▪▪▪

I found this on page ___480___ .

Order *the transformation of igneous rock into sedimentary rock.*

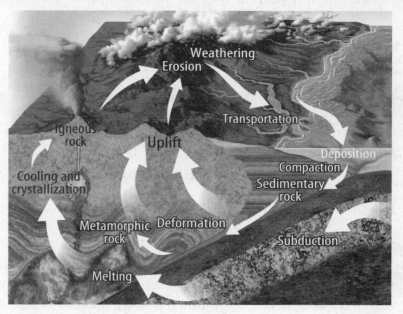

1. uplift
2. transportation
3. weathering
4. deposition
5. erosion
6. compaction

I found this on page ___482___ .

 Relate *plate tectonics to the* rock cycle.

Rock Cycle Factor	How It Relates to Plate Tectonics
Igneous rock formation	**happens where volcanoes occur and where plates move apart**
Metamorphic rock formation	**occurs from pressure where plates collide**
Uplift	**caused by colliding plates**
Formation of magma	**happens when plate movements push rock deep below Earth's surface**

Synthesize It If the rock cycle was compared to an engine, why could it be said that tectonic activity provides the fuel?

Accept all reasonable responses. Sample answer: The movement of Earth's plates,

and the volcanoes and faults that occur at plate boundaries, produce the pressures

that cause uplift and metamorphism. Tectonic activity keeps the rock cycle processes

going, like fuel keeps an engine running.

Chapter Wrap-Up

Now that you have read the chapter, think about what you have learned.

Use this checklist to help you study.

❑ Complete your Foldables® Chapter Project.

❑ Study your *Science Notebook* on this chapter.

❑ Study the definitions of vocabulary words.

❑ Reread the chapter, and review the charts, graphs, and illustrations.

❑ Review the Understanding Key Concepts at the end of each lesson.

❑ Look over the Chapter Review at the end of the chapter.

THE BIG IDEA **Summarize It** Reread the chapter Big Idea and the lesson Key Concepts. Why do you think the lesson topics appear in the order in which they are presented in the chapter? Lesson 1, about minerals, appears before Lesson 2, which is about rocks. Then Lesson 3 discusses the rock cycle and ends the chapter. Write a paragraph to explain your answer.

Accept all reasonable responses. Sample answer: It makes sense to learn about

minerals first, before learning about rocks, because rocks are made up of minerals.

Then, after you know what rocks are and how they form, it makes sense to learn

about the processes that change them over time.

_____

_____

_____

_____

_____

_____

Challenge *Think of what would happen to the rock cycle if Earth's tectonic plates stopped moving. Write a science fiction story about this idea. Share your story with your class.*

Name _____ Date _____

Plate Tectonics

 What is the theory of plate tectonics?

Before You Read

Before you read the chapter, think about what you know about plate tectonics. Record your thoughts in the first column. Pair with a partner, and discuss his or her thoughts. Write those thoughts in the second column. Then record what you both would like to share with the class in the third column.

Think	Pair	Share

Chapter Vocabulary

Lesson 1	Lesson 2	Lesson 3
NEW Pangaea continental drift **REVIEW** fossil	**NEW** mid-ocean ridge seafloor spreading normal polarity magnetic reversal reversed polarity **ACADEMIC** normal	**NEW** plate tectonics lithosphere divergent plate boundary transform plate boundary convergent plate boundary subduction convection ridge push slab pull

A Lesson Content Vocabulary page for each lesson is provided in the Chapter Resources Files.

Scan *Lesson 1. Then write three questions that you have about continental drift in your Science Journal. Try to answer your questions as you read.*

■■■ **Main Idea** ■■■

■■■■■■■■■■ **Details** ■■■■■■■■■

Pangaea
I found this on page _____495_____ .

Define Pangaea. *Include in your definition the name of the scientist who proposed the idea.*

Alfred Wegener described Pangaea as the single

supercontinent of which all present continents were

once a part.

I found this on page _____495_____ .

Summarize *the effect of* continental drift *on* Pangaea.
Continental drift caused Pangaea to break into parts that

spread away from one another across the surface of Earth.

Because of continental drift, Pangaea no longer exists. The

single piece of land broke into several smaller pieces.

Evidence That Continents Move
I found this on page _____496_____ .

Model *the stages of the breakup of* Pangaea. *Draw or describe each stage.*

Drawings should show a single landmass of any reasonable shape.

Beginning

Drawings should show the same landmass as in drawing 1, but broken into slightly separated pieces.

Early in the Process

Drawings should show the same-shaped pieces as in drawing 2, but the pieces should be spread farther apart and show some rotation.

Much Later

■ ■ ■ **Main Idea** ■ ■ ■   ■ ■ ■ ■ ■ ■ ■ ■ ■ ■ ■ **Details** ■ ■ ■ ■ ■ ■ ■ ■ ■ ■ ■

🔑 **Classify** *two examples of evidence that continents have moved during Earth's history. Write an explanation and give two examples for each kind of clue.*

I found this on page ___496___ .

I found this on page ___498___ .

Clue	Explanation	Examples
Climate clues	Fossil clues suggest that the past climates of some land areas were different; thus, the land was in a different location with regard to the equator. Some landmasses now in warm climates show evidence of past glacial activity.	coal in Antarctica; glacial grooves in India
Rock clues	Mountain ranges and rock formations on different continents have common origins.	Eruption evidence on Africa and South America match; Caledonian and Appalachian mountains match.

What was missing?
I found this on page ___499___ .

🔑 **Identify** *two reasons why scientists doubted Wegener's ideas.*

1. Wegener could not measure the movement of the continents.

2. Wegener could not explain what forces caused the continents to move.

🔑 **Analyze It** Many natural resources are mined from the rock beneath Earth's surface. Use what you have learned to explain how evidence found on one continent could be useful on another.

Sample answer: If resources are found along the edge of one continent, they might

also be found along the edge of another continent that adjoined it when Pangaea was

one large landmass.

Predict *three facts that will be discussed in Lesson 2 after reading the headings. Write your predictions in your Science Journal.*

■■■ **Main Idea** ■■■

Mapping the Ocean Floor

I found this on page ___503___.

■■■■■■■■ **Details** ■■■■■■■■

Assess *information about the ocean floor. Read the statements below. If the statement is true, write* true *on the line. If it is false, write* false *on the line and rewrite the underlined portion of the statement so that it is true.*

A device called an echo-sounder *can determine the depth of the ocean.*

true _____

Topographic maps of the seafloor made from ocean depth data reveal that the seafloor is almost completely flat.

false; vast mountain ranges stretch along the seafloor

Mid-ocean ridges are shorter than mountain ranges found on land.

false; longer than mountain ranges found on land

Seafloor Spreading

I found this on page ___504___.

🔑 **Sequence** *the process of* seafloor spreading.

The seafloor spreads at a mid-ocean ridge. Solid mantle material begins to ____**melt**____. This material is ____**less**____ dense than the surrounding solid rock.

⬇

The liquid ____**magma**____ rises through ____**cracks**____ in the crust and erupts from volcanic vents along the ____**mid-ocean ridge**____.

⬇

The magma, now called ____**lava**____, cools, solidifies, and forms a rock called ____**basalt**____.

⬇

Magma continues to rise and solidify. It pushes the newly-formed ____**crust**____ away from the ____**mid-ocean ridge**____. Younger, less dense, warmer rocks are found ____**close to**____ the ridge. Older, denser, cooler rocks are found ____**farther from**____ the ridge.

Lesson 2 | Development of a Theory (continued)

▪▪▪ Main Idea ▪▪▪

I found this on page ___504___ .

Development of a Theory
I found this on page ___506___ .

I found this on page ___507___ .

▪▪▪▪▪▪ Details ▪▪▪▪▪▪

🔑 **Summarize** *the importance of the idea of* seafloor spreading.

The idea of seafloor spreading provides a mechanism to

explain why continents move. Continents move with the

ocean crust as it spreads away from mid-ocean ridges.

Model normal polarity *and* reversed polarity *by drawing arrows in the diagrams below.*

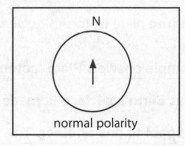

normal polarity

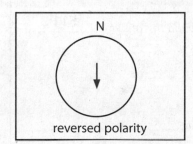

reversed polarity

Draw *the seafloor on either side of a* mid-ocean ridge. *Show the rocks that formed during times of* normal polarity *in blue. Show those that formed during times of* reversed polarity *in red. Then write a sentence to explain how* magnetic reversal *confirms the idea of* seafloor spreading.

Drawings should show a cross-section of the seafloor with a mid-ocean ridge in the middle. Parallel bands of alternating polarity should be mirrored on both sides of the ridge.

Sample answer: The magnetic stripes on both sides of

mid-ocean ridges match up. The ocean crust is made at the

ridges and is carried away in both directions.

🔑 **Connect It** Recall the questions that scientists had about Wegener's continental drift theory. Explain how seafloor spreading answers one or more of those questions.

Accept all reasonable responses. Sample answer: One of the questions was how the

continents were able to move through the solid rock of Earth's crust. The answer

explained by seafloor spreading is that the crust itself is moving, and that the

continents are "riding along" on the floating sections of crust.

Predict *three ideas that will be discussed in Lesson 3 after reading the headings. Write your predictions in your Science Journal.*

▪▪▪ **Main Idea** ▪▪▪

The Plate Tectonics Theory
I found this on page _____511_____ .

I found this on page _____511_____ .

I found this on page _____512_____ .

Plate Boundaries
I found this on page _____513_____ .

▪▪▪ **Details** ▪▪▪

State *the problem that scientists had with seafloor spreading.*
Sample answer: When new oceanic crust is made, it spreads out, taking up space. Scientists did not understand how new crust was not increasing the size of Earth.

Define plate tectonics. *Explain what the word* tectonic *means as part of your definition.*
Sample answer: Plate tectonics is a theory which states that Earth's surface is made of plates that move with respect to one another. The word tectonic means "builder" and refers to the forces that shape Earth's crust.

Identify *the layers of Earth involved in plate movements. Describe how these layers interact.*

Layer	Description
Lithosphere	consists of the crust and the solid, uppermost mantle
Asthenosphere	**layer that flows beneath the rigid lithosphere**

🔑 **Organize** *information about* divergent plate boundaries. *Use arrows to show how plates move relative to one another at this type of boundary.*

Type of Boundary	Description	Movement
Divergent	**forms where two plates separate; can exist in the middle of a continent or on the ocean floor**	← →

Main Idea ■■■ | ■■■■■■■■■■■■■■ Details ■■■■■■■■■■■■■

🔑 **Model** transform plate boundaries. *Either write a description or illustrate this type of plate interaction. Include arrows to show the direction of movement. Label the plates and the structures that result from the collisions.*

I found this on page ___514___ .

Drawings should show two plates that slide horizontally past each other.
Transform Plate Boundaries

I found this on page ___514___ .

Drawings should show the two plates folding and deforming to form mountains. Neither plate should be moving under the other.
Continent-to-Continent Collision

▪▪▪ **Main Idea** ▪▪▪ | ▪▪▪▪▪▪▪▪▪▪▪▪ **Details** ▪▪▪▪▪▪▪▪▪▪▪▪▪

Evidence for Plate Tectonics

I found this on page _____515_____ .

🔑 **Identify** *evidence for plate motion provided by* plate tectonics.

1. Satellites can measure how fast continents move.

2. location of earthquake activity explained

3. location of volcanic activity explained

4. location of mountains explained

Plate Motion

I found this on page _____516_____ .

Define convection, *and give an example of* convection *you have experienced in your everyday life.*

Definition: Convection is the circulation of material caused by differences in temperature and density.

Example: Accept all reasonable responses. Sample answers: air circulating in a heated room; water circulating in a pot on a stove; air currents in the atmosphere causing thunderstorms

I found this on page _____516_____ .

Explain *how* convection *occurs in the mantle by completing the sequence diagram.*

_____**Radioactive**_____ elements heat the inside of Earth.

⬇

The _____**heat**_____ is transferred from the _____**core**_____ to the _____**mantle**_____. _____**Convection**_____ currents form.

⬇

These currents in the asthenosphere move the _____**lithosphere**_____ above it.

⬇

In this way, _____**tectonic plates**_____ move in response to _____**the heating and cooling of mantle material**_____.

▪▪▪ **Main Idea** ▪▪▪ | ▪▪▪▪▪▪▪▪▪▪▪▪ **Details** ▪▪▪▪▪▪▪▪▪▪▪▪▪

I found this on page ___517___ .

🔑 **Describe** *the forces that cause plate motion.*

Force	Description
Basal drag	Convection currents drag the plates along as though on a conveyor belt.
Ridge push	Hot magma rises and solidifies at elevated ridges. Gravity pulls the rocks down and out of the way so that new seafloor can form.
Slab pull	The sinking plate, or slab, pulls on the rest of the plate as it descends into the mantle.

A Theory in Progress
I found this on page ___518___ .

Identify *four questions scientists have about* plate tectonics.

1. Why did the plates separate to begin with?

_____

2. Why do some earthquakes and volcanoes occur far

away from plate boundaries?

3. What forces dominate plate motion?

_____

4. What will scientists investigate next?

_____

🔑 **Synthesize It** What explanation can you offer for several volcanoes located in a line on the seafloor erupting over time to form islands?

Accept all reasonable responses. Sample answer: The volcanoes are probably

located near where two oceanic plates meet. As the older plate was subducted, it

melted. This melted material rose and formed the line of volcanoes. Over time, lava

built up to form islands.

Chapter Wrap-Up

Now that you have read the chapter, think about what you have learned.

Use this checklist to help you study.

❏ Complete your Foldables® Chapter Project.

❏ Study your *Science Notebook* on this chapter.

❏ Study the definitions of vocabulary words.

❏ Reread the chapter, and review the charts, graphs, and illustrations.

❏ Review the Understanding Key Concepts at the end of each lesson.

❏ Look over the Chapter Review at the end of the chapter.

 Summarize It Reread the chapter Big Idea and the lesson Key Concepts. Draw a world map showing how the continents might be arranged 100 million years from now. Label the landmasses on your map, and explain why you positioned them in the way that you did.

Accept all reasonable responses. Drawings and explanations should reflect

probable outcomes of plate tectonics, such as a widened Atlantic Ocean and smaller

Pacific Ocean. Students might also include collisions and rotations of recognizable

continental shapes.

Challenge *Suppose that you are designing a new scientific instrument to record or measure some geological data that previously could not be observed. Describe what your new super-technology could detect and how those discoveries might solve remaining mysteries of plate tectonics.*

Earthquakes and Volcanoes

THE BIG IDEA **What causes earthquakes and volcanic eruptions?**

Before You Read

Before you read the chapter, think about what you know about earthquakes and volcanoes. In the first column, write three things you already know about these natural events. In the second column, record three things that you would like to learn more about. When you have completed the chapter, think about what you have learned and complete the **What I Learned** *column.*

K What I Know	W What I Want to Learn	L What I Learned

Chapter Vocabulary

Lesson 1	Lesson 2
NEW earthquake fault seismic wave focus epicenter primary wave secondary wave surface wave seismologist seismometer seismogram **REVIEW** plate boundary convergent	**NEW** volcano magma lava hot spot shield volcano composite volcano cinder cone volcanic ash viscosity **ACADEMIC** dissolve

A Lesson Content Vocabulary page for each lesson is provided in the Chapter Resources Files.

Lesson 1 Earthquakes

Scan *Lesson 1. In your Science Journal, write three questions that you have about earthquakes. Try to answer your questions as you read.*

▪▪▪ **Main Idea** ▪▪▪

What are earthquakes?
I found this on page _____531_____ .

Where do earthquakes occur?
I found this on page _____532_____ .

I found this on page _____532_____ .

▪▪▪▪▪ **Details** ▪▪▪▪▪

🔑 **Define** earthquakes.

vibrations in the ground that result from movement along

breaks in Earth's lithosphere

🔑 **Summarize** *the distribution of* earthquakes *on Earth.*

Most earthquakes occur in the oceans and along the edges

of continents.

Categorize *information about the relationship between* earthquake *events and* plate boundaries.

Boundary Type	Depth of Earthquake	Other Details Sample answers
Convergent boundaries	very deep	most devastating earthquakes
Divergent boundaries	shallow	occur along the mid-ocean ridge system
Convergent boundaries involving two continents	varying depths	can result in the formation of large, deformed mountain ranges

I found this on page _____533_____ .

Illustrate *rock deformation, and write a short description of how this process works.*

Drawing	Description
Drawings should show a rock bending but not breaking.	Continuous force applied to a body of rock can cause the rock to change shape. This change can eventually result in the breaking of the rock.

Lesson 1 | Earthquakes (continued)

▪▪▪ Main Idea ▪▪▪

I found this on page __533__.

▪▪▪ Details ▪▪▪

Describe *each type of* fault.

Type of Fault	Description	Location
Strike-slip	Blocks slide horizontally past each other in opposite directions.	transform plate boundaries
Normal	Forces pull blocks apart. One block drops relative to the other.	divergent plate boundaries
Reverse	Forces push blocks together. One block is uplifted relative to the other.	convergent plate boundaries

I found this on page __534__.

Distinguish *between an* earthquake's focus *and its* epicenter.

Sample answer: The focus is the location where rocks first move along a fault. The epicenter is the location on Earth's surface directly above the focus.

Seismic Waves
I found this on page __535__.

Compare *the 3 types of* seismic waves. *Provide at least three details about each type.*

Type of Fault	Description Sample answers are shown.
Primary waves (P-waves)	cause rock particles to vibrate in same direction as waves travel; fastest waves; travel through solids and liquids
Secondary waves (S-waves)	cause rock particles to vibrate perpendicular to direction waves travel; speed between p-waves and surface waves; detected after p-waves; travel through solids only
Surface waves	cause rock particles to move in a rolling motion in same direction as waves travel; slowest waves; cause most surface damage

Lesson 1 | Earthquakes (continued)

▪▪▪ **Main Idea** ▪▪▪

Mapping Earth's Interior
I found this on page ___536___ .

Sample answers are shown.

I found this on page ___537___ .

I found this on page ___537___ .

▪▪▪ **Details** ▪▪▪

Identify *what scientists have discovered about Earth's interior by studying* seismic waves.

Inner and outer core: __The outer core is liquid, and the inner core is solid. The inner and outer cores are made mostly of iron and nickel.__

Mantle: __Using wave speed differences, scientists have been able to map convection currents in the mantle.__

Distinguish *between a* seismometer *and a* seismogram.

Seismometer	Seismogram
A seismometer measures ground motion and the distance and direction that seismic waves move.	The motion is recorded in a graphical illustration called a seismogram.

🔑 **Sequence** *the steps followed in locating an* earthquake's epicenter.

> Find the arrival time difference.
>
> Determine the __number of seconds__ between the appearance of the first __P-wave__ and the first __S-wave__ on the seismogram.

> Find the distance to the epicenter.
>
> Use a __graph__ to determine __distance__. Find the time difference on the __y-axis__. Read the distance from the epicenter on the __x-axis__.

> Plot the distance on the map.
>
> Draw a __circle__ around the seismometer location so that all points are the same distance from the station determined in Step 2.
>
> Repeat these steps for at least __two__ more seismometer locations. The epicenter is __the point where the three circles intersect__

154 Earthquakes and Volcanoes

Lesson 1 | Earthquakes (continued)

▪▪▪ **Main Idea** ▪▪▪

Determining Earthquake Magnitude

I found this on page ___538___ .

▪▪▪▪▪▪▪ **Details** ▪▪▪▪▪▪▪

Compare and contrast *the Richter magnitude scale, the moment magnitude scale, and the Modified Mercalli scale.*

> **Richter Magnitude Scale**
>
> The scale uses the amount of ___ground motion___
>
> at a given ___distance___ from an earthquake
>
> to determine ___magnitude___ .

> **All**
> Measure the size, or intensity, of an earthquake

> **Moment Magnitude Scale**
>
> Measures the ___total___ ___amount of energy___ released by an earthquake; energy released depends on:
>
> 1. the size of the ___fault___ ;
> 2. the ___motion___ that occurs;
> 3. the ___strength___ of the rocks.

> **Modified Mercalli Scale**
>
> Measures the ___amount___ ___of damage___ that results from ___shaking___ Determined based on ___descriptions of___ ___effects___
>
> Scale ranges from ___I___ to ___XII___

I found this on page ___540___ .

Record *four indicators that* seismologists *use to determine* earthquake *risk.*

1. ___past earthquake activity___
2. ___geology around a fault___
3. ___population density___
4. ___types of buildings in an area___

⊶ **Analyze It** Explain why two different earthquakes with the same Richter magnitude scale readings could have very different Modified Mercalli scale numbers.

___Sample answer: The Mercalli scale is based more on damage, which can depend on___

___how buildings were constructed or the density of the population, rather than actual___

___ground movement measured by the Richter scale.___

Lesson 2 Volcanoes

> **Predict** *three facts that will be discussed in Lesson 2 after reading the headings. Record your predictions in your Science Journal.*

▪▪▪ Main Idea ▪▪▪

▪▪▪▪▪▪▪▪▪▪▪ Details ▪▪▪▪▪▪▪▪▪▪▪

What is a volcano?
I found this on page __545__ .

Define volcano. *Include in your definition the term for the molten rock beneath Earth's surface.*

Sample answer: A volcano is a vent in Earth's crust

through which melted, or molten, rock flows. Molten rock

below Earth's surface is called magma.

How do volcanoes form?
I found this on page __545__ .

🔑 **Identify** *the cause of the formation of* volcanoes.

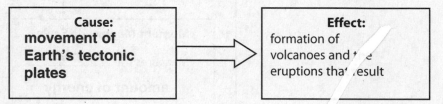

Cause: movement of Earth's tectonic plates	➡	Effect: formation of volcanoes and the eruptions that result

Sketch *the movement of plates where* volcanoes *occur.*

Area	Sketch
Convergent boundaries	Drawings should show two plates colliding, with the denser plate melting as it subducts beneath the less-dense plate. The resulting magma rises through cracks in the crust to form volcanoes.
Divergent boundaries	Drawings should show two plates moving apart, and magma rising up through the rift that forms between them.
Hot spots	Drawings should show a plume of mantle material under the crust, forming a volcano at the surface.

I found this on page __546__ .

I found this on page __546__ .

I found this on page __546__ .

Copyright © Glencoe/McGraw-Hill, a division of The McGraw-Hill Companies, Inc.

Lesson 2 | Volcanoes (continued)

▪▪▪ **Main Idea** ▪▪▪	▪▪▪▪▪▪▪▪▪▪▪▪ **Details** ▪▪▪▪▪▪▪▪▪▪▪▪
Where do volcanoes form? *I found this on page* ___547___ .	**Identify** *the location of most of the world's active* volcanoes. **Most volcanoes occur close to plate boundaries.**
I found this on page ___547___ .	**Explain** *the relationship between the Ring of Fire,* volcanoes, *and* plate boundaries. **Sample answer: The Ring of Fire represents an area of** **earthquake and volcanic activity that surround the Pacific** **Ocean and corresponds to convergent and divergent plate** **boundaries.**
I found this on page ___547___ .	**Record** *4 factors that scientists monitor to determine the likelihood of a volcanic eruption.* **Sample answers shown.** 1. **earthquake activity** 2. **changes in the shape of a volcano** 3. **gas emissions** 4. **past eruptive history of the volcano**
Types of Volcanoes *I found this on page* ___548___ .	🔑 **Identify** *the 2 characteristics scientists use to classify* volcanoes. 1. ____**shape**____ 2. ____**size**____
I found this on page ___548___ .	🔑 **Model** *the shapes and sizes of the 3 types of* volcanoes. *Label your drawings.* **Shield volcano:** Drawings should indicate a large volcano with gentle, sloping sides. **Cinder cone:** Drawings should indicate a small, steep-sided volcano. **Composite volcano:** Drawings should indicate a large, steep-sided volcano; they might include alternating layers of lava and ash.

■■■ **Main Idea** ■■■

Volcanic Eruptions
I found this on page ___549___ .

I found this on page ___549___ .

I found this on page ___550___ .

■■■■■ **Details** ■■■■■

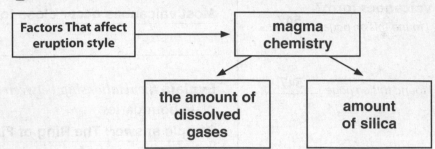

Identify *3 factors that affect eruption style.*

Factors That affect eruption style → **magma chemistry** → **the amount of dissolved gases** / **amount of silica**

Distinguish *among magmas with different silica content.*

Silica Content	Viscosity	Where these eruptions commonly occur
Low	low	mid-ocean ridges and hot spots
High	high	subduction zones and continental hot spots
Intermediate	intermediate	subduction zones and continental hot spots

Sequence *steps that lead to explosive eruptions as dissolved gases escape from magma.*

Magma moves toward the surface. ___Pressure___ caused by overlying rock ___decreases___ . The ability of gases to stay dissolved also ___decreases___ :

___Bubbles___ begin to form. As the magma rises, the ___bubbles___ become ___larger___ , and gas begins to ___escape___ .

It is more difficult for bubbles to escape from ___high-viscosity___ lavas. This combination can result in ___explosive___ eruptions.

Lesson 2 | Volcanoes (continued)

▪▪▪ **Main Idea** ▪▪▪ | ▪▪▪▪▪▪▪▪▪▪ **Details** ▪▪▪▪▪▪▪▪▪▪

Sample answers are shown.

Describe *four effects of volcanic activity.*

Activity	Effects
I found this on page __551__. Lava flows	**Although not usually deadly, lava flows can damage or destroy communities located near volcanoes.**
I found this on page __551__. Ash fall	**Ash is made of particles of pulverized glass. It can disrupt air traffic and affect air quality. Large quantities of ash can affect climate.**
I found this on page __551__. Mudflows	**Mudflows, formed when meltwater mixes with mud and ash, can bury towns and kill many people.**
I found this on page __552__. Pyroclastic flow	**Made of a mixture of hot gas, ash, and rock, these flows move quickly and burn everything in their path.**

Volcanic Eruptions and Climate Change

I found this on page __552__.

Identify *the effect of volcanic eruptions on climate.*

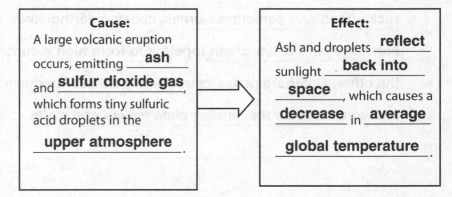

Cause:
A large volcanic eruption occurs, emitting **ash** and **sulfur dioxide gas**, which forms tiny sulfuric acid droplets in the **upper atmosphere**.

Effect:
Ash and droplets **reflect** sunlight **back into space**, which causes a **decrease** in **average global temperature**.

🔑 **Connect It** The Cascade Range in the northwestern United States has many volcanoes, including Mount St. Helens. These mountains are at a convergent plate boundary. Identify the type of volcano you would most expect to find in the Cascade Range and the nature of its eruptions.

Accept all reasonable responses. Sample answer: Because this is a convergent plate boundary, I would expect to find volcanoes that erupt magma high in silica. These eruptions would likely be explosive, as gases would have a difficult time escaping from the sticky lava. The type of volcano would likely be composite, as lava and ash would form large, steep-sided cones.

Earthquakes and Volcanoes

Chapter Wrap-Up

Now that you have read the chapter, think about what you have learned. Complete the **What I Learned** *column on the first page of the chapter.*

Use this checklist to help you study.

❏ Complete your Foldables® Chapter Project.

❏ Study your *Science Notebook* on this chapter.

❏ Study the definitions of vocabulary words.

❏ Reread the chapter, and review the charts, graphs, and illustrations.

❏ Review the Understanding Key Concepts at the end of each lesson.

❏ Look over the Chapter Review at the end of the chapter.

THE BIG IDEA **Summarize It** Reread the chapter Big Idea and the lesson Key Concepts. Use what you have learned about earthquakes and volcanoes to explain why these natural phenomena often occur in the same areas.

Accept all reasonable responses. Sample answer: Volcanic and earthquake activity

are associated with plate boundaries. As these plates move past each other, the

rocks bend and sometimes break, causing earthquakes. At other boundaries, plates

converge, and either crash together to form high mountains, or one subducts under

the other. Crashing plates cause earthquakes. Subducting plates cause earthquakes

and volcanoes as the sinking plate moves and melts.

_____

_____

_____

_____

_____

_____

Challenge *Use available resources to identify earthquake and volcanic activity over the last six months. Plot this data on a world map. What patterns can you identify?*

Clues to Earth's Past

 What evidence do scientists use to determine the ages of rocks?

Before You Read

Before you read the chapter, think about what you know about determining the ages of rocks. Record your thoughts in the first column. Pair with a partner, and discuss his or her thoughts. Then record what you both would like to share with the class in the third column.

Think	Pair	Share

Chapter Vocabulary

Lesson 1	Lesson 2	Lesson 3
NEW	**NEW**	**NEW**
fossil	relative age	absolute age
catastrophism	superposition	isotope
uniformitarianism	inclusion	radioactive decay
carbon film	unconformity	half-life
mold	correlation	
cast	index fossil	**REVIEW**
trace fossil		mineral
paleontologist		
ACADEMIC		
uniform		

A Lesson Content Vocabulary page for each lesson is provided in the Chapter Resources Files.

Lesson 1 Fossils

Scan *Lesson 1. Write three questions that you have about fossils in your Science Journal. Try to answer your questions as you read.*

▪▪▪ Main Idea ▪▪▪

▪▪▪ Details ▪▪▪

Evidence of the Distant Past

I found this on page ____565____.

 Define fossil. *Include two types of preserved clues in your definition.*

Fossils are the preserved remains or evidence of ancient living things.

I found this on page ____566____.

Summarize *the principles of* catastrophism *and* uniformitarianism.

Catastrophism	Uniformitarianism
Catastrophism credits changes to Earth to quick, violent events over a short time period.	Uniformitarianism states that geologic processes that occur today are similar to those that have occurred in the past; it credits changes to Earth to slower processes over a longer time.

Formation of Fossils

I found this on page ____567____.

Identify *factors that promote fossilization. Cross out terms that do not support the likelihood of* fossil *formation.*

buried quickly ~~soft tissue~~ ~~microscopic~~

~~decay easily~~ hard parts ~~very large~~

~~exposed~~ ~~rotting~~ ~~eaten~~

I found this on page ____567____.

Sequence *three probable steps of* fossil fish *formation.*

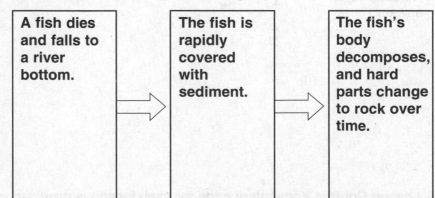

| A fish dies and falls to a river bottom. | → | The fish is rapidly covered with sediment. | → | The fish's body decomposes, and hard parts change to rock over time. |

▪▪▪ **Main Idea** ▪▪▪

▪▪▪▪▪▪▪▪▪ **Details** ▪▪▪▪▪▪▪▪▪

Types of Preservation

🔑 **Summarize** *the processes of* fossil *formation. Name and describe each process.*

I found this on page __568__ .

I found this on page __568__ .

I found this on page __568__ .

I found this on page __569__ .

I found this on page __569__ .

I found this on page __569__ .

Fossil Preservation	
Process	**Description**
Preserved remains	Actual remains of an organism are preserved in a substance that keeps it from being exposed to air or bacteria.
Carbon films	**Pressure on the buried organism drives off gases, leaving a thin outline of carbon.**
Mineral replacement	**Minerals in groundwater fill in pore spaces or replace tissues of dead organisms.**
Molds	**Sediment hardens around a buried organism; the organism leaves an impression.**
Casts	**A fossil copy is made when sediment or mineral deposits fill a mold of an organism.**
Trace fossils	**Evidence of the activity of an organism is preserved, such as footprints.**

Ancient Environments

I found this on page __570__ .

🔑 **Complete** *the concept below.*

If a fossil of an organism resembles a modern organism, **the ancient organism might have lived in a similar environment.**

I found this on page __571__ .

Classify *evidence of past climates.*

Climate	Evidence
Warm	**fossils of ferns and tropical plants**
Cool	**fossils of coarse grasses and mammoths**

🔑 **Connect It** Fossils provide clues to what happened in the ancient past. Identify a clue about what might have happened in the recent past in your current environment, and tell how long that clue is likely to last.

Accept all reasonable responses. Sample answer: The stump of a tree is evidence of

where a tree once grew. Depending on effects of the weather and the size of the tree,

the stump might be around for a few decades.

> **Predict** *three facts that will be discussed in Lesson 2 after reading the headings. Write your predictions in your Science Journal.*

▪▪▪ **Main Idea** ▪▪▪ | ▪▪▪▪▪▪▪▪▪▪▪▪▪ **Details** ▪▪▪▪▪▪▪▪▪▪▪▪▪

Relative Ages of Rocks

I found this on page __575__ .

🔑 **Explain** *why a single rock cannot be described in terms of* relative age.

Relative age is the age of rocks and geologic features with

respect to other nearby rocks and features. Other rocks

must be included in the comparison to describe a rock's

relative age.

🔑 **Model** *the principles of* relative age *dating below in drawings and descriptions.*

Concept	Drawing	Description
Superposition	Drawings should show multiple layers arranged oldest to youngest from bottom to top.	Layers of rock are arranged oldest to youngest from bottom to top.
Original horizontality	Drawings should show sediments deposited in flat layers. Students might also show the same layers tilted.	Layers of rock can be tilted or folded, but they originated as flat, horizontal layers.
Lateral continuity	Drawings should show same layers as above with the addition of a river cutting through the layers.	Layers of rock are deposited as flat sheets in all directions. Erosion can cut into the rock, but the order of layers does not change.
Inclusion	Drawings should show any rock shape with smaller fragments in the rock.	A piece of an older rock becomes part of a newer rock mass.

I found this on page __576__ .

I found this on page __576__ .

I found this on page __576__ .

I found this on page __577__ .

Lesson 2 | Relative-Age Dating (continued)

▪▪▪ **Main Idea** ▪▪▪ | ▪▪▪▪▪▪▪▪ **Details** ▪▪▪▪▪▪▪▪

I found this on page _____577_____ .

🔑 **Order** *the features in the illustration from youngest to oldest.*

dike   fault   inclusion   sedimentary layers

youngest
fault
dike
inclusion
sedimentary layer
oldest

Unconformities

I found this on page _____578_____ .

Define unconformity, *and identify and describe 3 types.*

Unconformity: **a surface where rock has worn away, producing a gap in the rock record**

Type: **disconformity**	Type: **angular** **unconformity**	Type: **nonconformity**
Description: **Younger sedimentary layers are deposited on top of older, horizontal sedimentary layers that have eroded.**	Description: **Sedimentary layers are deposited on top of tilted or folded sedimentary layers that have eroded.**	Description: **Younger sedimentary layers are deposited on older igneous or metamorphic rock layers that have eroded.**

Lesson 2 | Relative-Age Dating (continued)

••• **Main Idea** •••	••• **Details** •••

Correlation

I found this on page ____578____ .

🔑 **Complete** *the rock-dating concept in the diagram below.*

matching ____**rocks and fossils**____

+

separate ____**locations**____

=

____**correlation**____

I found this on page ____579____ .

Characterize *organisms that form* index fossils.

```
        Organisms that
        form index fossils
```

lived on Earth for short length of time	were abundant	lived in many locations

I found this on page ____579____ .

Analyze *the usefulness of* index fossils. *Write the correct terms.*

Index fossils allow scientists to learn ____**the relative ages**____ of

____**rock formations**____ that are very ____**far apart**____ or on different

____**continents**____ . Scientists ____**infer**____ that layers with

____**index fossils**____ found in ____**different locations**____

are of similar ____**age**____ .

🔑 **Synthesize It** Museums all over the world collect samples of rocks and fossils. What is the benefit to scientists of these collections?

Accept all reasonable responses. Sample answer: Because a great deal about Earth's

past is learned from comparisons, access to many samples collected from many

locations is helpful to scientists.

Lesson 3 | Absolute-Age Dating

Scan *Lesson 3. Read the lesson titles and bold words. Look at the pictures. Identify three facts that you discover about absolute-age dating. Write these facts in your Science Journal.*

▪▪▪ **Main Idea** ▪▪▪ | ▪▪▪▪▪▪ **Details** ▪▪▪▪▪▪

Absolute Ages of Rocks
I found this on page ___**583**___.

Define absolute age.

Absolute age: __**the numerical age, in years, of a rock or**__

__**other object**__

I found this on page ___**583**___.

Summarize absolute age *and relative age.*

> **Ways to describe the ages of objects**

| **Absolute Age** **numerical age determined using radioactivity** | **Relative Age** **age described with respect to another object or person** |

Atoms
I found this on page ___**584**___.

Describe *the makeup of an atom.*

An atom is the ___**smallest**___ part of an element that has all the properties of the element. Each atom contains smaller particles called ___**protons**___, ___**neutrons**___, and ___**electrons**___. ___**Protons**___ and ___**neutrons**___ are located in an atom's ___**nucleus**___. ___**Electrons**___ surround the nucleus.

I found this on page ___**584**___.

Define isotopes.

Isotopes: __**atoms of the same element that have different**__

__**numbers of neutrons**__

I found this on page ___**584**___.

Explain *how* radioactive decay *releases energy from unstable atoms.*

> ___**Radioactive**___ isotopes decay, releasing ___**energy**___
> and forming ___**new, more stable atoms**___.

| The element that decays is called the ___**parent**___ isotope. | The new element that forms is called the ___**daughter**___ isotope. |

••• Main Idea •••

I found this on page ___585___.

••• Details •••

🔑 **Calculate** *the change in* isotopes *during* radioactive decay.

	Percent Parent	Percent Daughter
Original materials	100	0
One half-life	50	50
Two half-lives	25	75
Three half-lives	12.5	87.5
After many more half-lives	close to 0	close to 0

Radiometric Ages

I found this on page ___586___.

🔑 **Describe** *why radiometric dating can be used to determine an object's age.*

Radiometric Dating

↓

Radioactive isotopes decay at a _____ **constant rate** _____,

so they can be used to measure _____ **age** _____.

↓

The ratio of _____ **parent** _____ isotope to _____ **daughter** _____ product is used as a measure.

I found this on page ___586___.

🔑 **Explain** *how radiocarbon dating uses decay to help determine age.*

Organism	Description
Alive	• The organism takes in _____ **C-14** _____. • The ratio of radioactive carbon, or _____ **C-14** _____ to _____ **C-12** _____, remains constant.
Dead _____	• _____ **C-14** _____ begins to decay. • The ratio of _____ **C-14** _____ to _____ **C-12** _____ changes.

⠿⠿⠿ Main Idea ⠿⠿⠿	**⠿⠿⠿⠿⠿⠿⠿ Details ⠿⠿⠿⠿⠿⠿⠿**

I found this on page ____586____ .

🔑 **Identify** *two reasons that radiocarbon dating can be used to measure the ages of once-living things accurately.*

1. **The ratio of C-14 to C-12 is used to determine how long the organisms have been dead.**

2. **With a half-life of 5,730 years, C-14 is useful for measuring the age of remains up to 50,000 years old.**

I found this on page ____587____ .

Explain *why radiometric dating is not useful for determining the age of sedimentary rock.*

Sample answer: Radioactive isotopes would probably measure the ages of the grains that make up the rock, not the time when the sediments were deposited.

I found this on page ____588____ .

Identify *five radioactive* isotopes *that can be used for dating rocks. Circle the two* isotopes *with the longest half-lives.*

1. **uranium-235**
2. **uranium-238**
3. **rubidium-87**
4. **potassium-40**
5. **thorium-232**

I found this on page ____588____ .

Summarize *the conclusions that scientists have made about Earth's age.*

Earth, the Moon, and meteorites formed at **about the same time** .	→	Radiometric dating of Moon rocks indicates that Earth is **4.5 billion** years old.

🔑 **Connect It** You find a piece of petrified wood. Explain whether radiocarbon dating could be used to date your find. If not, what could be used?

Sample answer: Petrified wood was once a living organism, and radiocarbon dating works on once-living objects. However, during the fossilization process, the organic material of the wood was replaced with rock-forming minerals, so radiocarbon dating would not work. Instead, radiometric dating with any of the other radioactive isotopes could be used.

Clues to Earth's Past

Chapter Wrap-Up

Now that you have read the chapter, think about what you have learned.

Use this checklist to help you study.

- ❏ Complete your Foldables® Chapter Project.
- ❏ Study your *Science Notebook* on this chapter.
- ❏ Study the definitions of vocabulary words.
- ❏ Reread the chapter, and review the charts, graphs, and illustrations.
- ❏ Review the Understanding Key Concepts at the end of each lesson.
- ❏ Look over the Chapter Review at the end of the chapter.

THE BIG IDEA

Summarize It Reread the chapter Big Idea and the lesson Key Concepts. To illustrate how geology is a type of detective work, write a summary of the kinds of changes that have affected Earth's surface according to geological clues. Identify at least three types of changes.

Accept all reasonable responses. Sample answers: Layers of rock are bent upward

to form mountains. Large cuts erode into rock and form canyons. Earth's climate

has changed over time.

_____

_____

_____

_____

_____

_____

_____

_____

_____

_____

Challenge *Build a three-dimensional model representing geological layers. Include features such as unconformities, inclusions, faults, and fossil clues in your model. Show and explain your model to your class.*

Name _____ Date _____

Geologic Time

 What have scientists learned about Earth's past by studying rocks and fossils?

Before You Read

Before you read the chapter, think about what you know about geologic time. Record your thoughts in the first column. Pair with a partner, and discuss his or her thoughts. Write those thoughts in the second column. Then record what you both would like to share with the class in the third column.

Think	Pair	Share

Chapter Vocabulary

Lesson 1	Lesson 2	Lesson 3	Lesson 4
NEW	**NEW**	**NEW**	**NEW**
eon	Paleozoic era	dinosaur	Holocene epoch
era	Mesozoic era	plesiosaur	Pleistocene epoch
period	Cenozoic era	pterosaur	ice age
epoch	inland sea		glacial groove
mass extinction	coal swamp	**REVIEW**	mega-mammal
land bridge	supercontinent	evaporated	
geographic isolation			**ACADEMIC**
			hypothesize

A Lesson Content Vocabulary page for each lesson is provided in the Chapter Resources Files.

Geologic History and the Evolution of Life

> **Scan** *Lesson 1. Then write three questions that you have about geologic history in your Science Journal. Try to answer your questions as you read.*

■■■ **Main Idea** ■■■

Developing a Geologic Time Line

I found this on page ___601___.

I found this on page ___601___.

I found this on page ___602___.

■■■ **Details** ■■■

Organize *units of geologic time from longest to shortest.*

eons	eras	periods	epochs

Longest ————————————————————▶ Shortest

Categorize *units of time in the Phanerozoic eon.*

	Eras	Periods
Phanerozoic	**Cenozoic**	Quaternary
		Tertiary
	Mesozoic	Cretaceous
		Jurassic
		Triassic
	Paleozoic	Permian
		Carboniferous
		Devonian
		Silurian
		Ordovician
		Cambrian

🔑 **Explain** *the relationship among fossils, rock layers, and the divisions of the geologic time scale.*

Rock layers contain different types of fossils. Fossils provide clues about living conditions during a given time span. Sudden changes in the fossil record mark major changes in the environment. Scientists use these major changes to divide geologic time into eras and periods.

Lesson 1 | Geologic History and the Evolution of Life (continued)

▪▪▪ Main Idea ▪▪▪ | ▪▪▪▪▪▪▪ Details ▪▪▪▪▪▪▪

Responses to Change
I found this on page ___603___ .

 Identify *the cause of a* mass extinction.

Cause: a catastrophic change in the environment that organisms cannot adapt to	→	Effect: many species on Earth become extinct within a short period of time

I found this on page ___603___ .

 Cite *an example of a catastrophic event linked to a* mass extinction.

Scientists hypothesize that a large meteoric impact

65.5 mya caused the mass extinction of the dinosaurs.

I found this on page ___604___ .

 Contrast *2 ways that geography can affect evolution.*

Land Bridge	Geographic Isolation
Two previously separated landmasses connect. Over time, organisms move across the bridge and evolve as they adapt to new environments.	A population is separated from the rest of its species by a physical barrier. The separated populations evolve with different characteristics.

Precambrian Time
I found this on page ___605___ .

Identify *the 3 eons of Precambrian time.*

1. Hadean	2. Archean	3. Proterozoic

<table>
<tr><td>

■■■ **Main Idea** ■■■

</td><td>

■■■■■■■■■■■■■■■ **Details** ■■■■■■■■■■■■■■

</td></tr>
</table>

I found this on page ___605___ .

Identify *Precambrian life-forms.*

Many were single-celled organisms, much like present-day

bacteria. About 600 mya, large, soft-bodied, multicellular

organisms appeared.

_____

_____

_____

I found this on page ___605___ .

Analyze *the effects of the Cambrian explosion on the fossil record.*

> There was a sudden appearance of ___new multicellular life-forms___
> _____ .

↓

> First organisms to have _____**hard body parts**_____ .

↓

> These _____**hard parts**_____ were more easily
> _____**preserved**_____ .

↓

> These hard parts left more _____**evidence**_____ in the
> _____**fossil record**_____ .

🔑 **Analyze It** Explain three ways that geologic time units compare with the time units you use to organize events in your life.

Accept all reasonable responses. Sample answer: Geologic time periods are vastly

longer than the seconds, minutes, hours, days, weeks, months, and years that I use

to organize events in daily life. The same types of geologic time units vary

significantly in length. For example, the Paleozoic, the Mesozoic, and the Cenozoic

are all eras, but the Paleozoic is longer than either the Mesozoic or the Cenozoic. This

contrasts with minutes, which are all 60 seconds long. The passing of geologic time

cannot be observed directly by people because the human life span is too short.

Predict *three facts that will be discussed in Lesson 2 after reading the headings. Record your predictions in your Science Journal.*

▪▪▪ **Main Idea** ▪▪▪

Early Paleozoic

I found this on page ____609____.

I found this on page ____609____.

▪▪▪▪▪▪▪▪▪▪ **Details** ▪▪▪▪▪▪▪▪▪▪

Summarize *the extent of the* Paleozoic era.

The Paleozoic era lasted for ____more than 290 million years____,

from ____542____ mya to ____250____ mya.

🔑 **Characterize** *the Early* Paleozoic era *in the organizer below.*

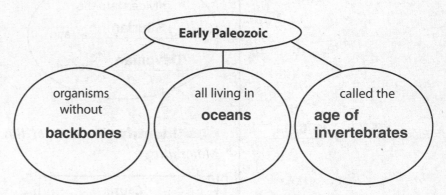

I found this on page ____610____.

🔑 **Contrast** *the Early* Paleozoic era *with the present.*

	Then	**Now**
Life on land	no land-based life-forms	diverse land-based life-forms
Amount of land mass	flooded by rising seas	much exposed

I found this on page ____610____.

🔑 **Point out** *the differences between present-day North America and the same landmass during the* Paleozoic era.

The North American continent is now situated fully north of

the equator and consists of mostly dry land. The same land

mass straddled the equator during the Paleozoic and was

mostly covered by shallow sea water.

Lesson 2 | The Paleozoic Era (continued)

▪▪▪ Main Idea ▪▪▪

Middle Paleozoic
I found this on page ___611___.

▪▪▪▪▪▪ Details ▪▪▪▪▪▪

🔑 **Characterize** *the Middle* Paleozoic era *in this organizer.*

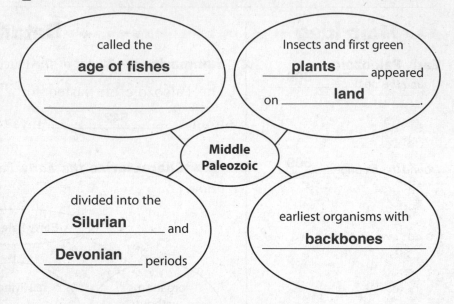

called the
age of fishes
_____

Insects and first green
plants _____ appeared
on _____ **land** _____.

Middle Paleozoic

divided into the
Silurian _____ and
Devonian _____ periods

earliest organisms with
backbones
_____

I found this on page ___611___.

🔑 **Identify** *the cause of the formation of the Appalachian Mountains.*

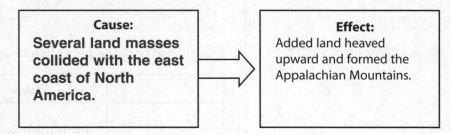

Cause:
Several land masses collided with the east coast of North America.

Effect:
Added land heaved upward and formed the Appalachian Mountains.

Late Paleozoic
I found this on page ___612___.

Characterize *the Late* Paleozoic era.

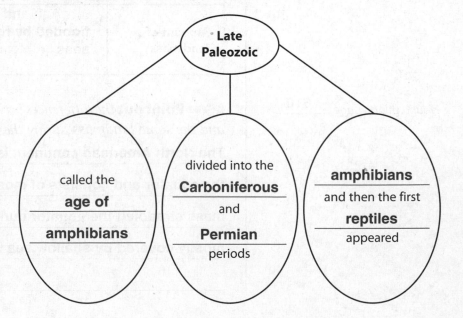

Late Paleozoic

called the
age of _____
amphibians

divided into the
Carboniferous _____
and
Permian _____
periods

amphibians _____
and then the first
reptiles _____
appeared

Lesson 2 | The Paleozoic Era (continued)

••• Main Idea •••	**••••••••••• Details ••••••••••••**

I found this on page __612__ .

Sequence *the development of coal in* coal swamps.

> 1. ___Dense forests___ grew in swamps along ___shallow inland seas___.
>
> 2. When ___plants___ died, they ___sank___ into tropical swamps (or coal swamps).
>
> 3. Plant matter changed into ___coal___ over time.

I found this on page __613__ .

🔑 **Define** *Pangaea, and explain its formation.*

Pangaea was a supercontinent formed near the end of the Paleozoic era when Earth's continents had moved together and formed one land mass, or supercontinent.

I found this on page __613__ .

🔑 **Summarize** *possible causes of the Permian mass extinction.*

Possible Cause	Related Effect
Formation of Pangaea	A decrease in marine habitat changed ocean currents, resulting in drier land interior.
Meteorite impact	Ash and rock in the atmosphere blocked sunlight and changed climate, resulting in collapsed food webs.
Volcanic eruption	Ash and rock in the atmosphere blocked sunlight and changed climate, resulting in collapsed food webs.

🔑 **Connect It** Summarize the overall evolution of life forms during the Paleozoic era.

Accept all reasonable responses. Sample answer: The earliest life forms were soft invertebrates that lived only in oceans. These were followed by animals with hard parts, then by vertebrates—fish. The first life forms on land were plants and insects. Then some fish adapted to breathe air and move about on land—the first amphibians. These amphibians gave way to the earliest reptiles, which could live and reproduce fully on land.

> **Scan** *Lesson 3. Read the lesson titles and bold words. Look at the pictures. Identify three facts that you discovered about the Mesozoic era. Record your facts in your Science Journal.*

▪▪▪ **Main Idea** ▪▪▪

Geology of the Mesozoic Era

I found this on page ____**617**____.

I found this on page ____**617**____.

▪▪▪ **Details** ▪▪▪

Arrange *the periods of the Mesozoic era in the table below.*

Periods of the Mesozoic Era		
Triassic	**Jurassic**	**Cretaceous**

from ____**251**____ mya   to ____**65.5**____ mya

Organize *information about the breakup of Pangaea.*

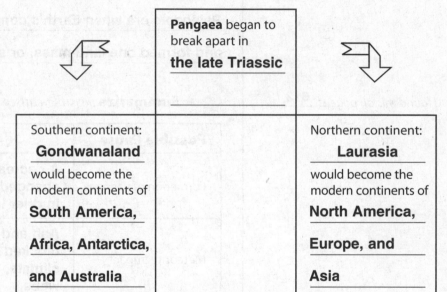

Pangaea began to break apart in **the late Triassic**

Southern continent: **Gondwanaland** would become the modern continents of **South America, Africa, Antarctica, and Australia**

Northern continent: **Laurasia** would become the modern continents of **North America, Europe, and Asia**

I found this on page ____**618**____.

Sequence *the events that formed the Atlantic Ocean.*

1. The climate was ____**warm**____ during the Mesozoic.
2. ____**Ocean levels**____ rose.
3. Pangaea began ____**to split apart**____.
4. ____**Ocean water**____ flowed onto ____**the continents**____.
5. ____**Narrow channels**____ formed.
6. As continents ____**moved apart**____, the channels became ____**oceans**____.

Lesson 3 | The Mesozoic Era (continued)

▪▪▪ **Main Idea** ▪▪▪

| ▪▪▪▪▪▪▪▪ **Details** ▪▪▪▪▪▪▪▪

I found this on page ___619___ .

Categorize *salt deposits in North America.*

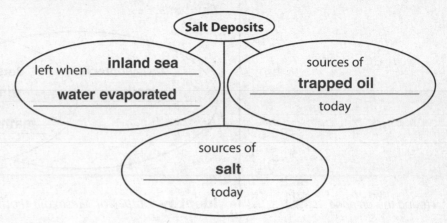

I found this on page ___619___ .

🔑 **Explain** *the geologic changes in North America during the Mesozoic.*

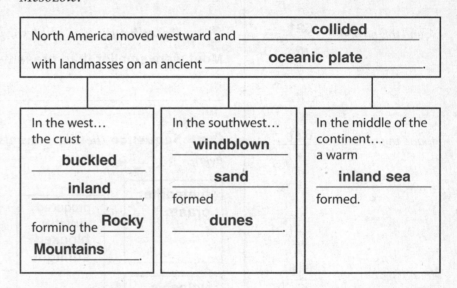

Mesozoic Life
I found this on page ___620___ .

Compare and contrast dinosaurs *with modern crocodiles.*

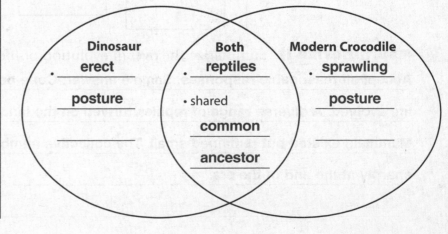

Copyright © Glencoe/McGraw-Hill, a division of The McGraw-Hill Companies, Inc.

Geologic Time **179**

■ ■ ■ **Main Idea** ■ ■ ■

I found this on page ___620___ .

I found this on page ___621___ .

I found this on page ___621___ .

I found this on page ___621___ .

■ ■ ■ ■ ■ ■ ■ ■ ■ ■ ■ ■ ■ ■ ■ ■ **Details** ■ ■ ■ ■ ■ ■ ■ ■ ■

🔑 **Compare and contrast** *the archaeopteryx with present-day birds.*

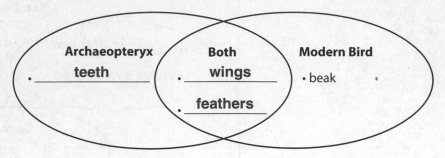

Archaeopteryx — • _____ teeth _____

Both — • _____ wings _____ • _____ feathers _____

Modern Bird — • beak

Identify *3 types of Mesozoic reptiles.*

Land	Sea	Air
dinosaurs	plesiosaurs	pterosaurs

🔑 **Describe** *the size of Mesozoic mammals.*

Most were smaller than present-day cats.

🔑 **Sequence** *the likely events of the Cretaceous extinction event.*

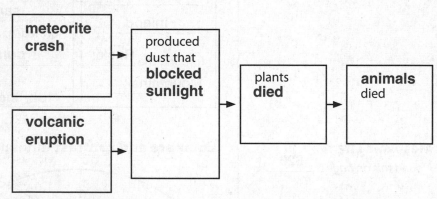

meteorite crash → produced dust that **blocked sunlight** → plants **died** → **animals** died

volcanic eruption →

🔑 **Summarize It** Summarize the overall evolution of life during the Mesozoic era.

Accept all reasonable responses. Sample answer: Cone-bearing and flowering plant

life evolved. A diverse range of reptiles thrived on the land, in the air, and in the seas.

Mammals existed but remained small. The collective number of species dropped

sharply at the end of the era.

Scan *Lesson 4. Read the lesson titles and bold words. Look at the pictures. Identify three facts that you discovered about the Cenozoic era. Record your facts in your Science Journal.*

■■■ **Main Idea** ■■■

Geology of the Cenozoic Era

I found this on page ____625____ .

■■■■■■■ **Details** ■■■■■■■

Examine *the extent of the Cenozoic era.*

The Cenozoic era began ____65.5____ million years ago,

at the end of the ____Cretaceous____ period of the

____Mesozoic____ era, and ____continues____ today.

I found this on page ____626____ .

Organize *information about the Cenozoic era below.*

fossil and rock record		most recent
well preserved	**Cenozoic**	**era**

Tertiary	divided into periods	**Quaternary**

divided into 5 epochs: **Paleocene, Eocene, Oligocene, Miocene, and Pliocene**	divided into 2 epochs: **Pleistocene and Holocene**

I found this on page ____626____ .

🔑 **Summarize** *Cenozoic mountain building activity.*

Range	Activity
Himalayas	**began forming as India crashed into Asia**
Alps	**began forming as Africa pushed into Europe**
Rockies	**continued to grow as North America pushed westward**
Cascades	**began to form as North America pushed westward**
Sierra Nevada	**began to form as North America pushed westward**
Appalachians	**erosion started in the Cenozoic and continues today**

■■■ **Main Idea** ■■■

I found this on page __627__ .

■■■■■■■■■ **Details** ■■■■■■■■■

Analyze *why the* ice age *that occurred during the* Pleistocene epoch *resulted in more dry land.*

Glaciers covered _____ **up to 30%** _____ of land surfaces.

↓

_____ **Water from oceans** _____ water was trapped _____ **in glaciers** _____ .

↓   ↓

Sea level _____ **dropped** _____ .

Inland seas _____ **drained** _____ .

**Cenozoic Life—
The Age of Mammals**

I found this on page __628__ .

🔑 **Order** *the evolution of life during the Cenozoic era.*

1. Flowering trees and plants _____ **spread out and diversified** _____ .
2. A new type of plant, _____ **grass** _____ , appeared.
3. New food sources allowed evolution of _____ **many animals** _____ .
4. _____ **Mammals** _____ thrived, and the Cenozoic became known as **the "age of mammals"**

I found this on page __628__ .

Contrast *the size of Cenozoic mammals with that of Mesozoic mammals.*

Mesozoic	Cenozoic
remained very small	grew very large

I found this on page __628__ .

Identify *three examples of* mega-mammals.

1. woolly mammoths	2. giant sloths	3. saber-toothed cats

Lesson 4 | The Cenozoic Era (continued)

▪▪▪ **Main Idea** ▪▪▪	▪▪▪▪▪▪▪▪▪▪▪▪▪▪▪ **Details** ▪▪▪▪▪▪▪▪▪▪▪▪▪▪▪

I found this on page ___629___ .

Analyze *the relationship between land bridges and evolution.*

Sample answer: Land bridges allowed ancestral animals to

migrate from one continent to another. When land bridges

disappeared, the separated populations evolved differently.

I found this on page ___630___ .

🔑 **Summarize** *the evolution and migration of humans.*

1. Human ancestors appeared nearly ___6 million___

   years ago in ___Africa___ .

2. ___Homo sapiens___ evolved during the

   ___Pleistocene___ epoch.

3. Early ___Homo sapiens___ migrated from ___Africa___

   to ___Europe___ and ___Asia___ .

4. They later migrated to ___North America___

   across a ___land bridge___ .

I found this on page ___630___ .

🔑 **Identify** *the cause of* Pleistocene *extinctions.*

Cause: organisms could not adapt quickly enough to climate change	→	Effect: extinction of mega-mammals

I found this on page ___630___ .

Describe *the changes occurring on present-day Earth.*

Sample answer: The planet is in a global warming climate

change.

🔑 **Analyze It** Explain how the Cenozoic fossil record differs from the Mesozoic and Paleozoic records and why.

Accept all reasonable responses. Sample answer: Because the Cenozoic time period

is recent in comparison with the others, its fossils are better preserved, so people

know more about the era's diversity of life.

Geologic Time

Chapter Wrap-Up

Now that you have read the chapter, think about what you have learned.

Use this checklist to help you study.

❏ Complete your Foldables® Chapter Project.

❏ Study your *Science Notebook* on this chapter.

❏ Study the definitions of vocabulary words.

❏ Reread the chapter, and review the charts, graphs, and illustrations.

❏ Review the Understanding Key Concepts at the end of each lesson.

❏ Look over the Chapter Review at the end of the chapter.

THE BIG IDEA **Summarize It** Reread the chapter Big Idea and the lesson Key Concepts. Write a description of how moving land masses and climate change have affected the evolution of life throughout Earth's history. How are these factors likely to affect life on Earth in the future?

Accept all reasonable responses. Answers should express that Earth's dynamic

environment causes the evolution of new species and the extinction of others.

Future events will continue to both increase and decrease the diversity of life over

time.

_____

_____

_____

_____

_____

_____

Challenge *On a long sheet of roll paper, draw a geologic time line to represent the Phanerozoic era, including all of its smaller units through the present. Write a detail and include a picture for each unit of geologic time represented.*

Interactions Within Ecosystems

 How do living things interact with each other and the environment?

Before You Read

Before you read the chapter, think about what you know about ecosystems. Record your ideas in the first column. Pair with a partner, and discuss his or her thoughts. Write those ideas in the second column. Then record what you both would like to share with the class in the third column.

Think	Pair	Share

Chapter Vocabulary

Lesson 1	Lesson 2	Lesson 3
NEW	**NEW**	**NEW**
habitat	producer	renewable resource
population	consumer	nonrenewable resource
community	detritivore	resource depletion
niche	food web	
predation	energy pyramid	**ACADEMIC**
symbiosis		enforce
carrying capacity	**REVIEW**	
	cellular respiration	

A Lesson Content Vocabulary page for each lesson is provided in the Chapter Resources Files.

> **Skim** *Lesson 1 in your book. Read the headings and look at the photos and illustrations. Identify three things you want to learn more about as you read the lesson. Record your ideas in your Science Journal.*

▪▪▪ Main Idea ▪▪▪ | ▪▪▪▪▪▪▪▪▪▪ Details ▪▪▪▪▪▪▪▪▪▪

Abiotic and Biotic Factors

I found this on page _____647_____ .

🔑 **Describe** *an ecosystem.*

Ecosystem
Definition: **all the living and nonliving parts of an environment in a given area**

Nonliving parts called: **abiotic factors**

Examples: **sunlight, soil, water, air**

Living or once-living parts called: **biotic factors**

Examples: **living organisms, their wastes, and decayed remains**

Habitats

I found this on page _____648_____ .

Relate *a habitat to an ecosystem.*

An ecosystem is all of the biotic and abiotic factors in a given area; a habitat is the area within an ecosystem that provides the biotic and abiotic factors an organism needs to survive and reproduce.

Populations and Communities

I found this on page _____648_____ .

Contrast *a population with a community.*

Population	Community
the number of individual organisms of the same species that live in an ecosystem at the same time	all the populations living in an area at the same time

■ ■ ■ **Main Idea** ■ ■ ■ | ■ ■ ■ ■ ■ ■ ■ **Details** ■ ■ ■ ■ ■ ■ ■

Interactions of Living Things

I found this on page ____**649**____ .

Define niche.

the way a species interacts with the abiotic and biotic

factors in its habitat to survive

_____

I found this on page ____**649**____ .

🔑 **Diagram** predation.

Predator **an organism that feeds on another organism**	→	Prey **an organism that gets eaten by a predator**

I found this on page ____**649**____ .

🔑 **Distinguish** *types of* symbiosis.

Symbiosis

Definition: **a close, long-term relationship between two species that usually involves an exchange of food or energy**

Mutualism **Both species benefit.**	Commensalism **One species benefits; the other is neither harmed nor benefited.**	Parasitism **One species benefits; the other is harmed.**
Example: **Bees collect nectar and pollinate flowers.**	Example: **Birds nest in trees.**	Example: **Striga plant roots rob a host plant of water.**

I found this on page ____**649**____ .

Identify *the roles of the two species in parasitic* symbiosis.

the species that benefits: _____**parasite**_____

the species that is harmed: _____**host**_____

▪▪▪ **Main Idea** ▪▪▪

I found this on page ___650___.

Sample answers are shown.

Population Changes
I found this on page ___650___

I found this on page ___651___.

I found this on page ___651___.

▪▪▪▪▪▪▪▪▪▪ **Details** ▪▪▪▪▪▪▪▪▪▪

🔑 **Point out** *two examples of competition.*

1. Trees compete with each other for sunlight.

2. Wolves compete with ravens for meat.

🔑 **Relate** *two effects of high* population *density.*

| **Cause** Individuals live closer together. | → | **Effects** · **increased competition** · **easier transmission of disease** |

🔑 **Break down** *the concept of* carrying capacity.

| population greater than carrying capacity | → | **Area becomes overpopulated; individuals move away or die out.** |

| **good growing conditions or the disappearance of competing species** | → | carrying capacity greater than population |

🔑 **Identify** *two possible effects of an instance of extinction of a population.*

| **Cause** A moose population dies from starvation. | → | **Possible Effect: Wolf population decreases because moose are not available as food.** |
| | → | **Possible Effect: Another plant-eating population increases without moose competition.** |

🔑 **Synthesize It** Write an example of how populations can occupy different niches within the same habitat.

Accept all reasonable responses. Sample answer: Giraffes, kudus, and steenboks all

eat leaves from the same trees, but they feed at different heights, or from different

locations on the tree.

Scan *Lesson 2. Read the lesson titles and bold words. Look at the pictures. Identify three facts you discovered about energy and matter. Record your facts in your Science Journal.*

▪▪▪ **Main Idea** ▪▪▪ | ▪▪▪▪▪▪▪▪▪▪▪▪ **Details** ▪▪▪▪▪▪▪▪▪▪▪▪

Food Energy

I found this on page _____**655**_____.

Characterize producers.

| Use **photosynthesis** or other chemical processes | → | Produce **their own food** |

Consumers

I found this on page _____**656**_____.

Contrast producers *with* consumers.

Producer	**Consumer**
organisms that can make their own food	organisms that cannot make their own food

I found this on page _____**656**_____.

Differentiate *4 types of* consumers. *Identify the types, and tell what they eat.*

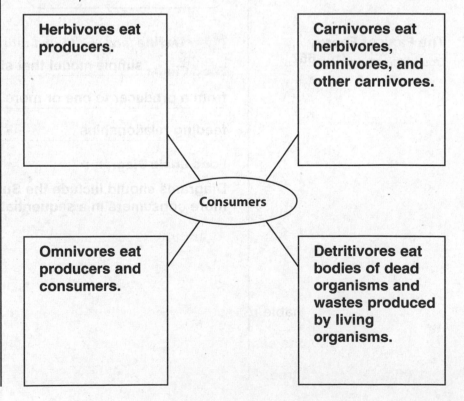

Herbivores eat producers.

Carnivores eat herbivores, omnivores, and other carnivores.

Consumers

Omnivores eat producers and consumers.

Detritivores eat bodies of dead organisms and wastes produced by living organisms.

Lesson 2 | Energy and Matter (continued)

▪▪▪ **Main Idea** ▪▪▪

I found this on page ___656___ .

▪▪▪ **Details** ▪▪▪

Classify *animals as types of* consumers.

Animal	Type
Aphid	**herbivore**
Raccoon	**omnivore**
Mole	**carnivore**
Termite	**detritivore**

I found this on page ___656___ .

Contrast *scavengers and decomposers, two types of* detritivores.

Detritivores

| **Scavengers** eat the bodies of animals killed by carnivores or omnivores | **Decomposers** microscopic; cause the decay of dead organisms or wastes |

The Flow of Energy

I found this on page ___657___ .

Define *food chain, and draw a diagram of a food chain.*

Food Chain: simple model that shows how energy moves

from a producer to one or more consumers through

feeding relationships

Food Chain Diagram:

Diagrams should include the Sun, a producer, and one or more consumers in a sequential relationship.

▪▪▪ **Main Idea** ▪▪▪

I found this on page ___657___ .

I found this on page ___658___ .

▪▪▪▪▪▪▪▪ **Details** ▪▪▪▪▪▪▪▪

🔑 **Define** food web, *and draw a diagram of a* food web.

Food Web: model of energy transfer that can show how the food chains in a community are interconnected

_____

Food Web Diagram:

Diagrams should include the Sun, one or more producers, and multiple consumers in interconnected relationships.

🔑 **Model** *an* energy pyramid. *Write an explanation below your drawing.*

Accept all reasonable diagrams. Students should show a pyramid with at least three levels, beginning with producers at the bottom, in the highest abundance, and advancing through a level with fewer herbivores to a level with the fewest carnivores.

Explanations should demonstrate understanding that as

energy moves through a food chain, some is used by the

organisms at each level and, thus, is not passed on.

■■■ **Main Idea** ■■■ | ■■■■■■■■■■■■■■■■ **Details** ■■■■■■■■■■■■■■

Cycling Materials

🔑 **Analyze** *how matter cycles through ecosystems.*

	Description of Cycle
Nitrogen	• Certain bacteria convert ___**nitrogen gas**___ into ___**nitrogen compounds**___ in the soil. • Plants and other ___**producers**___ use the ___**nitrogen compounds**___ to make ___**proteins**___. • ___**Animals**___ eat plants. • ___**Decaying organic matter**___ and waste return nitrogen compounds to ___**soil**___. • Other bacteria convert ___**nitrogen compounds**___ into ___**nitrogen gas**___, which is released into the air.
Water	• Surface water (and ___**transpiration**___ from plants) ___**evaporates**___ into the ___**atmosphere**___. • It ___**condenses**___ and forms ___**clouds**___. • Water falls to the surface as ___**precipitation**___. • ___**Plants**___ absorb water; ___**animals**___ consume plants.
Oxygen and Carbon Dioxide	• ___**Cellular respiration**___, ___**combustion**___, and ___**decomposition**___ release carbon dioxide into the ___**atmosphere**___. • Plants take in ___**carbon dioxide**___ through their leaves. • ___**Photosynthesis**___ releases ___**oxygen**___ into the atmosphere. • Plants and animals take in ___**oxygen**___ for ___**cellular respiration**___

I found this on page ___**659**___ .

I found this on page ___**660**___ .

I found this on page ___**661**___ .

🔑 **Connect It** Describe how you are part of the oxygen and carbon dioxide cycles.

I breathe in oxygen from the air, which my body uses in cellular respiration. I exhale

carbon dioxide back into the atmosphere, which is absorbed and used by plants.

Predict *three facts that will be discussed in Lesson 3 after reading the headings. Record your predictions in your Science Journal.*

■■■ **Main Idea** ■■■ | ■■■■■■■■■■■■■■■ **Details** ■■■■■■■■■■■■■■■

Affecting the Environment

I found this on page ___665___ .

🔑 **Describe two** *examples of living organisms affecting the environment.*

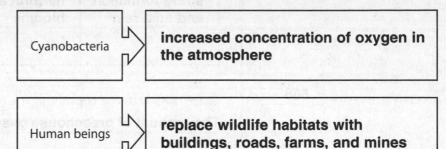

| Cyanobacteria ➔ | increased concentration of oxygen in the atmosphere |

| Human beings ➔ | replace wildlife habitats with buildings, roads, farms, and mines |

I found this on page ___666___ .

Contrast renewable resources *with* nonrenewable resources.

Renewable Resources	Nonrenewable Resources
resources that can be replaced by natural processes at least as quickly as they are used	natural resources that are used up faster than they can be replaced by natural processes

I found this on page ___666___ .

Explain *which type of resource described above is at risk for* resource depletion *and why.*

Nonrenewable resources; a resource that is used faster

than it can be replaced can be exhausted in an area.

I found this on page ___667___ .

Express *the cause and effect of the Montreal Protocol.*

CFCs were severely damaging the ozone layer. The

protocol phased out CFC use worldwide. Further damage

to the ozone layer was avoided.

▪▪▪ **Main Idea** ▪▪▪ | ▪▪▪▪▪▪▪▪ **Details** ▪▪▪▪▪▪▪▪

I found this on page ___667___ .

🔑 **Evaluate** *unintended consequences of three human activities on the environment.*

Fossil Fuels	Chemical Fertilizers	CFCs
smog formation and acid rain	harmful algae blooms	damage to the ozone layer

I found this on page ___668___ .

🔑 **Explain** *the concept of a carbon footprint.*

The amount of greenhouse gases emitted by a person, an

organization, an event, or a product is that entity's carbon

footprint.

I found this on page ___668___ .

🔑 **Express** *possible consequences of global climate change.*

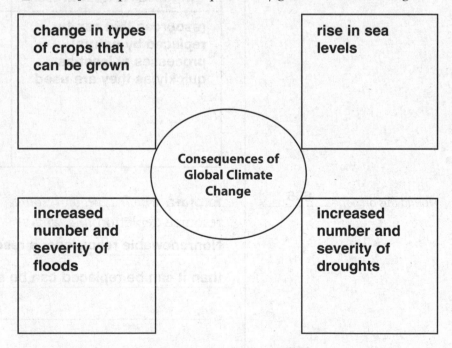

change in types of crops that can be grown

rise in sea levels

Consequences of Global Climate Change

increased number and severity of floods

increased number and severity of droughts

Protecting the World
I found this on page ___668___ .

Record *three methods of generating electricity that do not rely on fossil fuels.*

1. wind turbines

2. solar panels

3. underwater turbines

▪▪▪ **Main Idea** ▪▪▪ | ▪▪▪▪▪▪▪▪▪▪▪▪▪▪▪ **Details** ▪▪▪▪▪▪▪▪▪▪▪▪▪

I found this on page ____669____ .

🗝️ **Distinguish** *three environmental laws enacted in the United States.*

The Endangered Species Act: __lists species threatened or__ __endangered with extinction, designates habitat to protect__ __them, and outlaws actions that would harm them__

The Clean Air Act: __gives the EPA power to create emission__ __standards for cars, industries, and power plants__

The Clean Water Act: __regulates discharge of pollutants into__ __waterways__

I found this on page ____670____ .

Describe *the 5Rs for keeping the environment healthy.*

Action	Description
Restore	**Bring back damaged habitats and ecosystems to their original state.**
Rethink	**Reconsider the way people carry out daily tasks (for example, generate electricity).**
Reduce	**Reduce waste and pollution by using fewer resources.**
Reuse	**Repair broken items and invent new uses for old items instead of throwing them away.**
Recycle	**Process things so they can be used again for another purpose.**

🗝️ **Connect It** Think of an action you observe where you live that affects an ecosystem. Describe how one or more of the 5Rs can be used to protect the health of the ecosystem.

__Accept all reasonable responses. Sample answer: I often see plastic grocery bags__

__and other litter along the side of the road on my way to school. I can take part in a__

__clean up effort; I can also recycle any plastic bags I bring home or take my own__

__reusable bags to the grocery with me so I don't use any plastic bags at all.__

Chapter Wrap-Up

Now that you have read the chapter, think about what you have learned.

Use this checklist to help you study.
- ❏ Complete your Foldables® Chapter Project.
- ❏ Study your *Science Notebook* on this chapter.
- ❏ Study the definitions of vocabulary words.
- ❏ Reread the chapter, and review the charts, graphs, and illustrations.
- ❏ Review the Understanding Key Concepts at the end of each lesson.
- ❏ Look over the Chapter Review at the end of the chapter.

THE BIG IDEA **Summarize It** Reread the chapter Big Idea and the lesson Key Concepts. Summarize the parts of an ecosystem, how energy and matter cycle through ecosystems, and how human actions affect ecosystems.

Accept all reasonable responses. Sample answer: An ecosystem contains all the biotic and abiotic factors in a given area. Ecosystems provide the habitats for all living organisms. Organisms get the resources they need from their individual niches within their habitats. The amount of matter on Earth is constant, and it moves through cycles that include organisms, the atmosphere, and Earth itself. Producers are organisms that make their own food using energy from the Sun and chemical processes; consumers are organisms that get the energy they need by eating producers. Organisms are affected by their environments, and they also affect their environments. Humans build a lot of things and use a lot of resources that affect the environment and the habitats of many organisms in both expected and unintended ways. The 5Rs outline ways that humans can behave to protect the environment.

Challenge *Do research to find out about endangered species whose habitats are in areas near where you live. Choose one species, and design a poster about it. Include images and captions that tell about the species, its habitat, what environmental factors have caused it to be at risk, and how it is being protected. Display your poster in your classroom.*

Biomes and Ecosystems

 How do Earth's biomes and ecosystems differ?

Before You Read

Before you read the chapter, think about what you know about biomes and ecosystems. Record your thoughts in the first column. Pair with a partner, and discuss his or her ideas. Write those ideas in the second column. Then record what you both would like to share with the class in the third column.

Think	Pair	Share

Chapter Vocabulary

Lesson 1	Lesson 2	Lesson 3
NEW	**NEW**	**NEW**
biome	salinity	ecological succession
desert	wetland	climax community
grassland	estuary	pioneer species
temperate	intertidal zone	eutrophication
taiga	coral reef	
tundra		**REVIEW**
		community

A Lesson Content Vocabulary page for each lesson is provided in the Chapter Resources Files.

Scan *Lesson 1. Read the headings and bold words. Look at the pictures. Identify three facts that you discovered about land biomes. Record your facts in your Science Journal.*

■ ■ ■ **Main Idea** ■ ■ ■   ■ ■ ■ ■ ■ ■ ■ ■ **Details** ■ ■ ■ ■ ■ ■ ■ ■

Land Ecosystems and Biomes

I found this on page __683__ .

Define biome.

Biome: __a geographic area on Earth that contains__

__ecosystems with similar biotic and abiotic features__

_____

I found this on page __683__ .

Identify *biotic and abiotic features. Circle biotic features in blue. Circle abiotic features in red.*

air **R**	birds **B**	water **R**
insects **B**	sunlight **R**	soil **R**
mosses **B**	trees **B**	mammals **B**

I found this on page __683__ .

Identify *Earth's 7 major land* biomes.

1. __desert__

2. __grassland__

3. __tropical rain forest__

4. __temperate rain forest__

5. __temperate deciduous forest__

6. __taiga__

7. __tundra__

I found this on page __684__ .

Define *a desert.*

Desert: _____ __a biome that receives very little rain__ _____

_____

I found this on page __684__ .

Identify *factors that describe deserts. Circle the best choices.*

rainfall: (low)/ high

daytime temperatures: (hot)/ cold

nighttime temperatures: hot /(cold)

soil   (thin)/ thick

Lesson 1 | Land Biomes (continued)

▪▪▪ **Main Idea** ▪▪▪ | ▪▪▪▪▪ **Details** ▪▪▪▪▪

I found this on page **684** .

Describe *plant and animal adaptations to* deserts.

Plants: **Shallow roots absorb water quickly; stems store water; small leaves or spines reduce water loss.**

Animals: **avoid activity during hottest times of the day**

I found this on page **684** .

🔑 **Identify** *one way that humans impact* deserts.

Sample answers: Cities, farms, and recreational areas use valuable water; people and livestock damage slow-growing plants.

I found this on page **685** .

Define grassland.

Grassland: **a biome where grasses are the dominant plants**

I found this on page **685** .

Students might also list the crops rye and barley.

Organize *information about* grassland biomes.

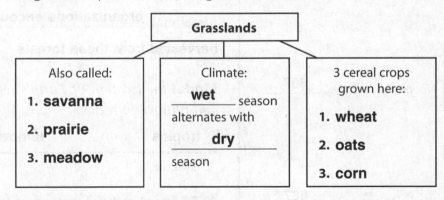

Grasslands		
Also called:	**Climate:**	**3 cereal crops grown here:**
1. **savanna**	**wet** season alternates with **dry** season	1. **wheat**
2. **prairie**		2. **oats**
3. **meadow**		3. **corn**

I found this on page **685** .

Students might also write insects, birds, rabbits, prairie dogs, snakes, hawks, ferrets, or coyotes in the left column. Students should circle lions, wild dogs, and if listed, wolves, snakes, hawks, ferrets, and coyotes.

Identify *animals common in* grasslands. *Circle any that you know are predators.*

North American Grassland	African Savanna	Australian Grassland
1. bison	1. giraffes	1. wild dogs
2. elk	2. zebras	2. kangaroos
3. wolves	3. lions	3. wallabies

I found this on page **685** .

🔑 **Explain** *one way that humans impact* grasslands.
People plow large areas to grow cereal crops.

■■■ Main Idea ■■■ | **■■■■■■■■■ Details ■■■■■■■■■■**

I found this on page ___686___ .

🔑 **Summarize** *4 features of tropical rain forests.*

1. Weather: <u>warm and wet all year</u>

2. Soil: <u>shallow and erodes easily</u>

3. Sunlight: <u>little sunlight reaches forest floor</u>

4. Biodiversity: <u>contains half of Earth's species</u>

I found this on page ___686___ .

Sample answers are shown.

Identify *living things in tropical rain forests.*

Plants: <u>tall leafy trees, vines, orchids; few plants live on the</u>

<u>forest floor</u>

Animals: <u>parrots, toucans, snakes, frogs, jaguars, ocelots,</u>

<u>fruit bats, birds, and insects</u>

I found this on page ___686___ .

🔑 **Evaluate** *human impact on tropical rain forests.*

Harmful: <u>have cleared more than half of tropical rain</u>

<u>forests for lumber, farms, and ranches</u>

Beneficial: <u>organizations encourage less use of wood</u>

<u>harvested from these forests</u>

I found this on page ___687___ .

Model *the location of Earth's regions. Locate the tropics, polar, and* temperate *regions.*

tropics	temperate	polar
equator		pole

←————————————————————————————→

I found this on page ___687___ .

🔑 **Point out** *the features of* temperate *rain forests.*

1. Winters: <u>mild and rainy</u>

2. Summers: <u>cool and foggy</u>

3. Soil: <u>rich and moist</u>

4. Common plants: <u>trees that can grow very large; ferns,</u>

<u>mosses, vines, and small flowering plants</u>

I found this on page ___687___ .

Students might also list cedar and fir.

Record *three examples of trees common to* temperate *rain forests.*

1. <u>spruce</u> **2.** <u>hemlock</u> **3.** <u>redwood</u>

Lesson 1 | Land Biomes (continued)

■■■ **Main Idea** ■■■ | ■■■■■■■■■■■ **Details** ■■■■■■■■■■■

I found this on page _____687_____ .

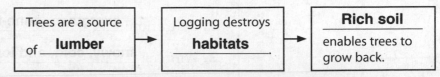 **Summarize** *the impact of logging on* temperate *rain forests.*

| Trees are a source of __lumber__ . | → | Logging destroys __habitats__ . | → | **Rich soil** enables trees to grow back. |

I found this on page _____688_____ .

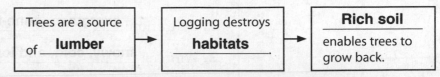 **Point out** *the features of a* temperate *deciduous forest.*

1. Winters: __cold and snowy__

2. Summers: __hot and humid__

3. Soil: __rich, supports diverse plant growth__

I found this on page _____688_____ .

Organize *information about adaptations to seasonal changes in* temperate *deciduous forests.*

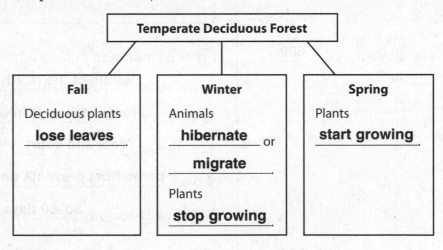

Temperate Deciduous Forest

Fall
Deciduous plants __lose leaves__

Winter
Animals __hibernate__ or __migrate__ .
Plants __stop growing__

Spring
Plants __start growing__

I found this on page _____688_____ .

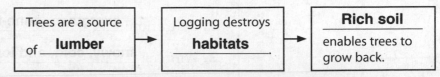 **Evaluate** *human impact on* temperate *deciduous forests.*

Past	Now
Thousands of acres of forest cleared for cities and farms.	**Much of the clearing of forests has stopped, and some have grown back.**

▪▪▪ **Main Idea** ▪▪▪ | ▪▪▪▪▪ **Details** ▪▪▪▪▪

I found this on page _____689_____ .

🔑 **Point out** *five features of the* taiga biome.

1. Location: <u>northern hemisphere</u>

2. Definition: <u>evergreen (cone-bearing) forest biome</u>

3. Winters: <u>snowy, cold, and long</u>

4. Summers: <u>short, warm, and moist</u>

5. Soil: <u>thin and acidic</u>

I found this on page _____689_____ .

🔑 **Evaluate** *human impact on the* taiga.

Cause	➡	Effect
cutting trees for lumber		**reduces habitat**

I found this on page _____689_____ .

🔑 **Summarize** *features of the* tundra.

1. Location: <u>south of the North Pole; high mountains</u>

2. Winters: <u>long, dark, and freezing</u>

3. Summers: <u>cool and short</u>

4. Soil: <u>permafrost prevents deep root growth</u>

5. Growing season: <u>50–60 days long</u>

I found this on page _____689_____ .

🔑 **Evaluate** *human impact on the* tundra.

Cause	➡	Effect
drilling for oil and gas		**can interrupt migratory patterns**

🔑 **Synthesize It** Identify three features that all land biomes share.

Accept all reasonable responses. Sample answer: All of Earth's biomes have plant and animal life that are adapted to their environment. All biomes have wet/dry or cold/warm seasonal changes. All biomes have been changed because of human activity.

Lesson 2 Aquatic Ecosystems

Predict *three facts that will be discussed in Lesson 2 after reading the headings. Record your predictions in your Science Journal.*

■■■ Main Idea ■■■

Aquatic Ecosystems
I found this on page ____693____ .

I found this on page ____693____ .

I found this on page ____693____ .

I found this on page ____694____ .

Sample answers are shown.

■■■ Details ■■■

Interpret *the definition of aquatic ecosystems, and identify the 4 major types.*

Aquatic ecosystems: water ecosystems

1. freshwater   3. wetland

2. estuary   4. ocean

Identify *four important abiotic factors in aquatic ecosystems.*

1. temperature   3. sunlight

2. dissolved oxygen   4. salinity

🔑 **Compare** *streams and rivers.*

	Stream	River
Water movement	fast-flowing	slower-moving
How formed	underground springs or runoff	streams flow together
Clarity of water	clear	can be muddy
Oxygen level	high	lower than stream
Nutrient level	low	higher than stream
Animals	trout, crayfish, and insects	snails and catfish
Plants	willow and cottonwood	water-loving plants
Human impact	1. water used for irrigation and drinking 2. energy from flowing water used to generate electricity 3. runoff can pollute rivers and streams.	

▪▪▪ **Main Idea** ▪▪▪ | ▪▪▪▪▪▪▪▪▪▪▪▪▪ **Details** ▪▪▪▪▪▪▪▪▪▪▪▪▪

I found this on page ___695___ .

Sample answers are shown.

 Compare and contrast *ponds and lakes.*

Alike	Different
1. contain freshwater that is not flowing downhill	1. lakes are larger and deeper than ponds
2. form in low places	2. pond are higher in nutrients
3. surrounded by plants	3. sunlight reaches the bottom of most ponds, but not lakes

I found this on page ___695___ .

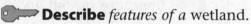 **Detail** *two ways in which humans impact ponds and lakes.*

1. fill in to create land for homes

2. runoff disrupts food webs

I found this on page ___696___ .

 Describe *features of a* wetland.

Definition: aquatic ecosystems that have a thin layer of water covering soil that stays wet most of the time

Physical description: form at the edges of lakes and ponds and in low areas; can be freshwater, or saltwater

Benefit to living things: important breeding grounds for many species; birds use wetlands to rest, feed, or nest; wetlands filter waste materials from water

Human impact: In the past, wetlands were drained to build roads or houses; now they are being preserved and restored.

I found this on page ___697___ .

 Complete *information about* estuaries.

Definition	ecosystems that form where a stream or river empties into a body of salt water
Benefit to humans	help protect coastal land from flooding and erosion; filter pollutants from the water
Human impact	People have drained and filled estuaries; this act reduces habitat and exposes the coastline to flooding and storm damage.

▪▪▪ **Main Idea** ▪▪▪ | ▪▪▪▪▪▪▪▪▪▪▪▪▪ **Details** ▪▪▪▪▪▪▪▪▪▪▪▪▪▪

I found this on page ____698____ .

🔑 **Summarize** *information about ocean ecosystems.*

Accept all reasonable responses. Sample answers are shown.

> **Open Ocean**
>
> Description: **high salinity; very deep water extends from the edges of the continental shelves to the deepest part of the ocean; zones based on availability of light**
>
> Living things: **Photosynthetic organisms live only in sunlit zone; many fish live in the twilight zone; some organisms live in the dark zone near cracks in the ocean floor.**
>
> Human impact: **Animals become entangled in trash or mistake it for food; overfishing threatens many fish species.**

I found this on page ____699____ .

Accept all reasonable responses. Sample answers are shown.

> **Ocean Ecosystems**

> **Coastal Oceans**
>
> Description: **shallow water that covers the continental shelves and intertidal zone**
>
> Living things: **organisms benefit from nutrients washed in from rivers and streams; organisms in intertidal zone adapt to changing conditions**
>
> Human impact: **easily polluted by runoff and oil spills**

> **Coral Reefs**
>
> Description: **underwater structures found in shallow tropical oceans made from the skeletons of tiny, soft-bodied animals**
>
> Living things: **high biodiversity**
>
> Human impact: **Pollution, overfishing, and harvesting of coral threaten these reefs.**

🔑 **Connect It** Trace the path of water from a stream to an estuary. Explain why prevention of pollution in streams is important to the health of estuaries.

Accept all reasonable responses. Sample answer: A stream forms from and collects runoff as it flows. Streams join and form rivers. Eventually, the water enters the estuary. There, the sediments, nutrients, and other pollutants carried by the streams and rivers are deposited. The pollutants can affect living things that depend on the estuary for breeding grounds and food. Thus, keeping streams free of pollutants ultimately helps keeps rivers and estuaries pollution free.

Skim *Lesson 3 in your book. Read the headings and look at the photos and illustrations. Identify three things you want to learn more about as you read the lesson. Record your ideas in your Science Journal.*

■■■ **Main Idea** ■■■

How Land Ecosystems Change

I found this on page _____**703**_____ .

I found this on page _____**703**_____ .

I found this on page _____**704**_____ .

Students should circle lichens.

■■■ **Details** ■■■

🔑 **Define** ecological succession.

Ecological succession: **the process of one ecological**

community gradually changing into another

Relate *how a stable climate affects plant life in a* climax community.

As plants die, new plants of the same species grow in their

places.

Sequence *the primary succession of a lava-covered landscape. Circle the* pioneer species.

After a volcano erupts, lava cools and hardens

into _____**bare rock**_____ .

(Lichen) spores _____ carried on the wind settle on the rock. Lichens break down the

_____**rock**_____ and add _____**nutrients**_____

to the soil.

Spores of ____**mosses**____ and ____**ferns**____ germinate. These organisms add to the

_____**soil**_____ when they die. Soil

can now hold _____**water**_____ .

After many years, _____**soil**_____ is deep and

has enough _____**nutrients**_____ to support

____**trees**____ , ____**grasses**____ and

____**shrubs**____ . ____**Animals**____ move in.

Eventually, the area becomes a _____**climax**_____

_____**community**_____

▪▪▪ **Main Idea** ▪▪▪ | ▪▪▪▪▪▪▪▪▪▪ **Details** ▪▪▪▪▪▪▪▪▪▪

I found this on page _____705_____ .

🔑➤**Draw** *an example of a disturbed landscape and how secondary succession produced a* climax community *in the same area.*

Drawings should show landscape that has been built on, farmed, or disturbed in some way.	Drawings should show a climax community in the same area; the drawing should include mature trees.
Before	After

How Freshwater Ecosystems Change
I found this on page _____706_____ .

🔑➤ **Sequence** *aquatic succession*

1. Aquatic succession begins with a body of freshwater.

2. Sediments and decaying organisms build up and form soil. The soil slowly fills the body of water.

3. Eventually, the body of water disappears, and a land ecosystem results.

I found this on page _____706_____ .

Define eutrophication, *and explain how humans contribute to it.*

Eutrophication: the process of a body of water becoming nutrient-rich

How humans contribute: Sample answer: When fertilizers and other forms of pollution high in nutrients enter a body of water, nutrient levels increase. Populations of microscopic organisms increase and use up much of the dissolved oxygen in the water, leaving less oxygen for other living things. Fish and other organisms die. Their decaying bodies speed succession.

🔑➤**Connect It** Use the idea of succession to explain why a pond in a farmer's field might be gone in 50 years.

Accept all reasonable responses. Sample answer: Ponds undergo succession. Sediments carried by rainwater and the decaying bodies of plants and animals accumulate on the bottom of the pond, building up soil. Plants begin to grow in the soil and contribute to filling the pond. In 50 years, the area where the pond is might become dry land.

Biomes and Ecosystems

Chapter Wrap-Up

Now that you have read the chapter, think about what you have learned.

Use this checklist to help you study.

❏ Complete your Foldables® Chapter Project.

❏ Study your *Science Notebook* on this chapter.

❏ Study the definitions of vocabulary words.

❏ Reread the chapter, and review the charts, graphs, and illustrations.

❏ Review the Understanding Key Concepts at the end of each lesson.

❏ Look over the Chapter Review at the end of the chapter.

THE BIG IDEA

Summarize It Reread the chapter Big Idea and the lesson Key Concepts. Analyze the information you have learned about biomes. Compare and contrast two land biomes.

Students should identify the two biomes they are comparing and state their

similarities in climate and seasonal conditions. Students should contrast the

location and biodiversity of each biome. They should compare and contrast the

impact of humans in each biome.

_____

_____

_____

_____

_____

_____

_____

_____

_____

_____

Challenge *Illustrate the steps in the succession of a lawn to a climax community. Include explanatory captions with your illustrations.*

Name _____ Date _____

Environmental Impacts

 How do human activities impact the environment?

Before You Read

Before you read the chapter, think about what you know about how human activities affect the environment. Record your ideas in the first column. Pair with a partner, and discuss his or her thoughts. Write those thoughts in the second column. Then record what you both would like to share with the class in the third column.

Think	Pair	Share

Chapter Vocabulary

Lesson 1	Lesson 2	Lesson 3	Lesson 4
NEW population carrying capacity	**NEW** deforestation desertification urban sprawl reforestation reclamation **REVIEW** runoff **ACADEMIC** dispose	**NEW** point-source pollution nonpoint-source pollution	**NEW** photochemical smog acid precipitation particulate matter global warming greenhouse effect Air Quality Index

A Lesson Content Vocabulary page for each lesson is provided in the Chapter Resources Files.

Predict *three facts that will be discussed in Lesson 1 after reading the headings. Record your predictions in your Science Journal.*

▪▪▪ **Main Idea** ▪▪▪ | ▪▪▪▪▪▪▪▪▪▪ **Details** ▪▪▪▪▪▪▪▪▪▪

Population and Carrying Capacity

I found this on page ____720____ .

Determine *causes and effects to the human* population *trend of the last two centuries.*

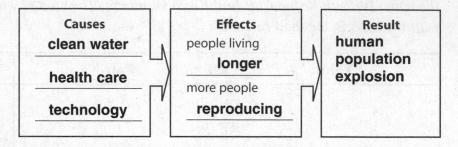

Causes	Effects	Result
clean water	people living	human
health care	**longer**	population
technology	more people	explosion
	reproducing	

I found this on page ____720____ .

Draw *a graph to represent human* population *growth since the year 1000.*

Graph should show a gradual increase to one billion in 1800, and a steep spike to six billion in 2000.

I found this on page ____720____ .

🔑 **Relate** *the consequence of* population *growth to at least three resources that people need to live.*

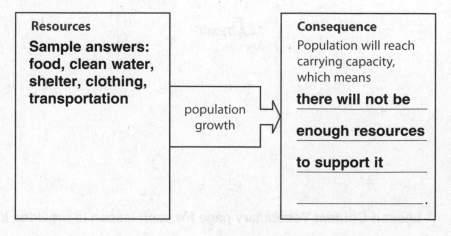

Resources	Consequence
Sample answers: food, clean water, shelter, clothing, transportation	Population will reach carrying capacity, which means
	there will not be
	enough resources
	to support it

population growth

▪▪▪ **Main Idea** ▪▪▪ | ▪▪▪▪▪▪▪▪▪▪ **Details** ▪▪▪▪▪▪▪▪▪

I found this on page ___720___.

Students might reverse the arrows to show that as human population decreases the availability of natural resources increases, but remind them that many natural resources are nonrenewable.

Diagram *the correlation between human* population *and natural* resources. *Draw pointers to change the labels into arrows, and then explain the relationship.*

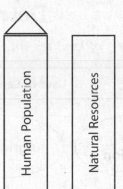

Explanation:
As human population increases, the availability of natural resources decreases.

Impact of Daily Actions
I found this on page ___721___.

🔑 **Characterize** *the environmental impact factors related to taking a hot shower.*

Factor	Connection	Environmental Impact
Metal pipes	mining	**Mining can contribute to pollution and habitat destruction.**
Cotton towels	agriculture	**Fertilizers can affect water quality.**
Hot water	energy consumption	**Burning fossil fuels pollutes the atmosphere.**

I found this on page ___721___.

Identify *elements of the environment that humans affect.*

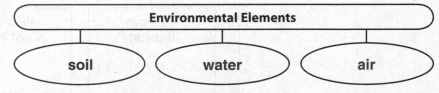

🔑 **Connect It** Evaluate the impact of an activity you perform daily.

Accept all reasonable responses. Sample answer: Riding the school bus: The bus is

built of metals and plastics that require mining and manufacturing, which disturb

habitats and consume energy. The bus burns diesel fuel, which contributes to air

pollution. The road the bus drives on is made of asphalt, which comes from oil.

Scan *Lesson 2. Read the lesson titles and bold words. Look at the pictures. Identify three facts you discovered about the effects of using land resources. Record your facts in your Science Journal.*

■■■ **Main Idea** ■■■ | ■■■■■■■■■■ **Details** ■■■■■■■■■■

Using Land Resources
I found this on page _____725_____ .

Identify *3 uses of land resources.*

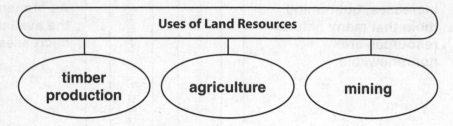

Uses of Land Resources

- timber production
- agriculture
- mining

I found this on page _____725_____ .

Classify *information about forest resources.*

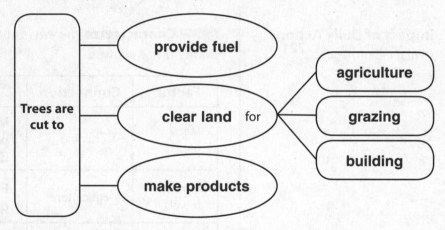

Trees are cut to
- provide fuel
- clear land   for
  - agriculture
  - grazing
  - building
- make products

I found this on page _____725_____ .

🔑 **Sequence** *the consequences of* deforestation.

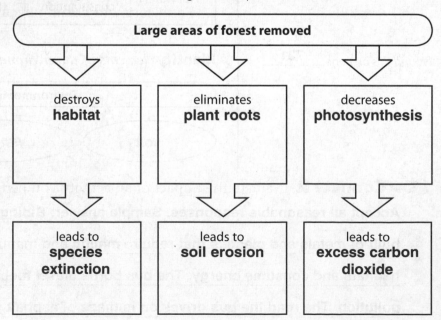

Large areas of forest removed

| destroys **habitat** | eliminates **plant roots** | decreases **photosynthesis** |

| leads to **species extinction** | leads to **soil erosion** | leads to **excess carbon dioxide** |

∎∎∎ **Main Idea** ∎∎∎

I found this on page _____726_____ .

Sample answers are shown.

I found this on page _____726_____ .

I found this on page _____727_____ .

∎∎∎∎ **Details** ∎∎∎∎

🔑 **Sequence** *the nitrogen cycle. Describe the elements of the process as they are numbered in the illustration.*

1 Plants use nitrogen compounds to make proteins.
2 Bacteria on plant roots **change nitrogen into usable forms.**
3 Decomposition releases nitrogen into soil and air.
4 Animals eat plants; their waste returns nitrogen compounds to soil.
5 Lightning changes some nitrogen gas into usable forms.
6 Fertilizers and grazing livestock add nitrogen to the environment.
7 Excess nitrogen **pollutes water.**

Relate *land uses to possible negative effects.*

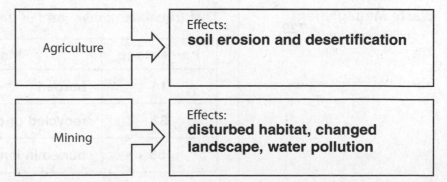

Agriculture → Effects: **soil erosion and desertification**

Mining → Effects: **disturbed habitat, changed landscape, water pollution**

••• **Main Idea** ••• ┊ ••••••••••• **Details** •••••••••

Construction and Development

I found this on page ___728___ .

Categorize *information about* urban sprawl.

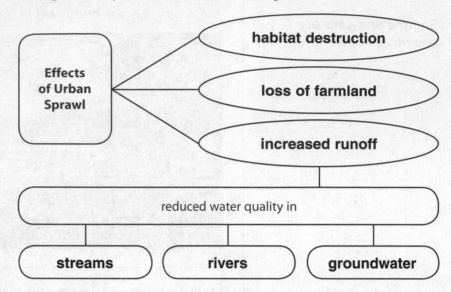

Effects of Urban Sprawl → habitat destruction

loss of farmland

increased runoff → reduced water quality in → streams, rivers, groundwater

I found this on page ___728___ .

Sequence *trends of vehicle use and roads in the United States.*

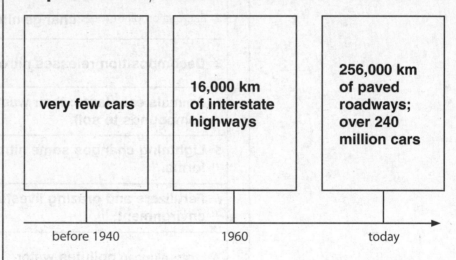

| very few cars | 16,000 km of interstate highways | 256,000 km of paved roadways; over 240 million cars |

before 1940   1960   today

I found this on page ___728___ .

Express *two functions of green space in urban environments.*

1. __recreation__   2. __decreased runoff__

Waste Management

I found this on page ___729___ .

Differentiate *management of trash in the United States.*

Percentage	Method of Disposal
14	burned
31	recycled or composted
55	buried in landfills

Lesson 2 | Impacts on the Land (continued)

▪▪▪ Main Idea ▪▪▪

I found this on page __729__ .
Sample answers are shown.

I found this on page __729__ .
Sample answers are shown.

Positive Actions
I found this on page __730__ .

I found this on page __731__ .

▪▪▪▪▪▪▪▪▪▪ Details ▪▪▪▪▪▪▪▪▪▪

🔑 **Identify** *three design elements of a landfill that aid in avoiding pollution.*

1. Clay and dirt cover prevent trash from blowing away.

2. Wells monitor groundwater quality.

3. Liquid waste is collected and treated so that it is not so hazardous.

Characterize *hazardous waste.*

Can affect:	Examples
· soil	Medical industry:
· air	· __needles__ and __bandages__
· water	Households:
· living things	· __batteries__ and __motor oil__

🔑 **Compare** *reforestation and* reclamation.
Both restore land that has been negatively impacted by human activity. Reforestation involves planting trees to replace those that have been cut or burned; reclamation involves replacing soil and reintroducing vegetation destroyed by mining.

🔑 **Restate** *the "three Rs" that lessen human impact on the land.*
1. __reducing__   2. __reusing__   3. __recycling__

🔑 **Analyze It** Imagine you are a member of a committee in your community that makes decisions about land use. A large area of land with some vacant buildings is given to your city. What questions must you consider in deciding what to do with the land?

Accept all reasonable responses. Questions might include: What habitats are affected by the buildings there now and any others we might want to build? What kinds of resources must we use to build on the land or to remove the buildings that are there now? What is the present condition of the land in terms of pollution?

Skim *Lesson 3 in your book. Read the headings and look at the photos and illustrations. Identify three things you want to learn more about as you read the lesson. Record your ideas in your Science Journal.*

■ ■ ■ ■ **Main Idea** ■ ■ ■   ■ ■ ■ ■ ■ ■ ■ ■ ■ ■ **Details** ■ ■ ■ ■ ■ ■ ■ ■ ■ ■

Water as a Resource

I found this on page ____735____ .

🔑 **Categorize** *uses of water in the United States.*

Percentage	Use
<3	livestock, mining, aquaculture
5	industry
11	public supply
34	agricultural irrigation
48	power plants

Sources of Water Pollution

I found this on page ____736____ .

Sequence *the path of water in the water cycle. Draw a circle around the stage in the process where most water pollution occurs.*

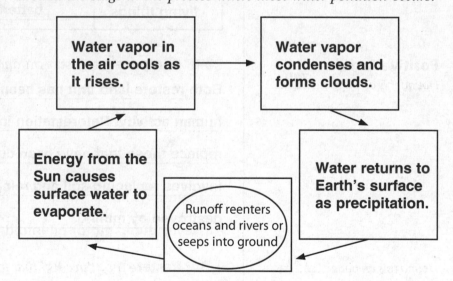

Water vapor in the air cools as it rises.

Water vapor condenses and forms clouds.

Energy from the Sun causes surface water to evaporate.

Runoff reenters oceans and rivers or seeps into ground

Water returns to Earth's surface as precipitation.

I found this on page ____736____ .

Contrast point-source pollution *and* nonpoint-source pollution.

Point-source	Nonpoint-source
Definition: **pollution from a single, identifiable source**	Definition: **pollution from several widespread sources that can't be traced to a single location**
Examples: **runoff from mines or an oil spill**	Examples: **runoff from farms and urban areas**

Sample answers are shown.

▪▪▪ **Main Idea** ▪▪▪ | ▪▪▪▪▪▪▪▪▪▪▪▪▪ **Details** ▪▪▪▪▪▪▪▪▪▪▪▪▪

Positive Actions

I found this on page ____738____ .

🔑 **Explain** *how it would be possible for the Cuyahoga River to catch fire. Then describe the positive action that resulted from it.*

Explanation: __Chemical-soaked litter floating on the river__ __caught fire.__

Action: __Canada and the United States made agreements to__ __prevent pollution and clean up the Great Lakes.__

I found this on page ____739____ .

🔑 **Describe** *two United States laws that help protect and maintain water quality.*

Law: **Clean Water Act**	Law: **Safe Drinking Water Act**
Description: **regulates sources of water pollution, including sewage systems**	Description: **protects supplies of drinking water throughout the country**

I found this on page ____739____ .

Sample answers are shown.

🔑 **Record** *three actions individuals can take to protect and improve water quality.*

1. __Use alternative cleaning products that do not include__ __toxins.__

2. __Never dump motor oil into drains or on the ground.__

3. __Take shorter showers to conserve water.__

🔑 **Synthesize It** Explain why cooperation between individuals, communities, and nations is necessary for water quality preservation.

__Accept all reasonable responses. Sample answer: Bodies of water run through or__ __span the borders of multiple countries. Pollutants travel with the water, regardless of__ __where the flow originates, so pollutants can enter water in one country but end up in__ __another.__

Impacts on the Atmosphere

Predict *three facts that will be discussed in Lesson 4 after reading the headings. Record your predictions in your Science Journal.*

■■■ **Main Idea** ■■■ | ■■■■■■■■■ **Details** ■■■■■■■■■

Importance of Clean Air
I found this on page _____743_____.

Explain *why clean air is important.*

Many organisms breathe air to stay alive. Air that is not

clean can harm the body.

Types of Air Pollution

🔑 **Differentiate** *types of air pollution.*

I found this on page _____743_____.

I found this on page _____744_____.

I found this on page _____744_____.

I found this on page _____744_____.

I found this on page _____744_____.

Type	Source	Problem
Photochemical smog	nitrogen and carbon compounds from the burning of fossil fuels	forms a brown haze in the air
Acid precipitation	nitrogen and sulfur from the burning of fossil fuels	Many trees and plants can't survive in highly acidic soil.
Particulate matter	solid particles, such as smoke, dust and dirt, from volcanoes, forest fires, and human activity	Inhaling causes coughing, difficulty breathing, and other respiratory problems.
CFCs	air conditioners and refrigerators made before 1996	CFCs destroy the ozone molecules that absorb harmful UV rays.
Carbon monoxide	vehicles, industry, wood burning and gas stoves	Breathing this gas reduces the amount of oxygen that reaches tissues and organs.

▪▪▪ **Main Idea** ▪▪▪ | ▪▪▪▪▪▪▪▪▪▪▪▪ **Details** ▪▪▪▪▪▪▪▪▪▪▪▪▪

Global Warming and the Carbon Cycle

I found this on page _____**745**_____ .

🔑 **Organize** *information about* global warming.

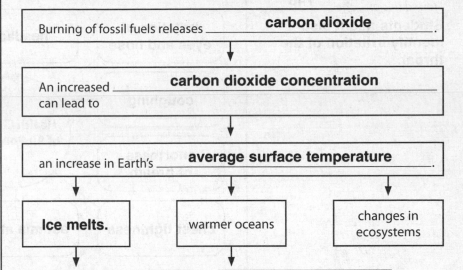

Burning of fossil fuels releases _____**carbon dioxide**_____ .
↓
An increased _____**carbon dioxide concentration**_____ can lead to
↓
an increase in Earth's _____**average surface temperature**_____ .

Ice melts.	**warmer oceans**	**changes in ecosystems**

Sea level rises.	**increase in storms**

coastal flooding	**intensity**	**frequency**

I found this on page _____**746**_____ .

Diagram *the* greenhouse effect. *Include Earth, Earth's atmosphere, and the Sun. Draw arrows to represent thermal energy.*

Drawing should show thermal energy from the Sun passing through Earth's atmosphere, reflecting off Earth's surface, and bouncing off the upper atmosphere back to the surface in repeated succession.

■■■ **Main Idea** ■■■ | ■■■■■■■■ **Details** ■■■■■■■■

Health Disorders

I found this on page ___746___ .

Students might also identify irritation of the throat.

🔑 **Identify** *ten ill health effects of air pollution.*

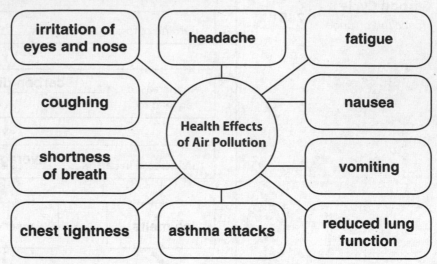

irritation of eyes and nose

headache

fatigue

coughing

Health Effects of Air Pollution

nausea

shortness of breath

vomiting

chest tightness

asthma attacks

reduced lung function

I found this on page ___747___ .

Interpret *air quality data.*

AQI Value for Ozone	What It Means
0 to 50	Air quality is good, and no preventative action is needed.
51 to 100	Air quality is moderate, and sensitive people should limit outdoor activity.
101 to 150	Air quality is unhealthy for sensitive groups, so they should limit outdoor activity.
151 to 200	Air quality is unhealthy for everyone; all groups should limit outdoor activity.
201 to 300	Air quality is very unhealthy. Sensitive groups should stay indoors, and others should limit outdoor activity.

I found this on page ___747___ .

Associate *ozone near Earth's surface with health problems.*

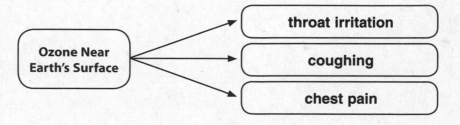

Ozone Near Earth's Surface

throat irritation

coughing

chest pain

Lesson 4 | Impacts on the Atmosphere (continued)

■■■ **Main Idea** ■■■ | ■■■■■■■■■ **Details** ■■■■■■■■■

Positive Actions
I found this on page ___748___ .

🔑 **Compare** *international initiatives to reduce air pollution.*

Montreal Protocol	Kyoto Protocol
190 countries have agreed to phase out the use of CFCs.	184 countries have agreed on the reduction of emissions of greenhouse gases.

I found this on page ___748___ .

🔑 **Characterize** *the Clean Air Act.*

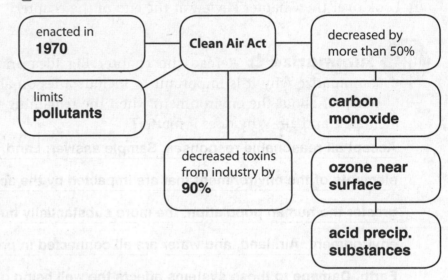

enacted in **1970** — Clean Air Act — decreased by more than 50%

limits **pollutants**

carbon monoxide

decreased toxins from industry by **90%**

ozone near surface

acid precip. substances

I found this on page ___748___ .

Record *three renewable energy resources.*

1. __solar power__
2. __wind power__
3. __geothermal energy__

I found this on page ___748___ .

Assess *the benefits of a hybrid car.*

more	less
energy efficient	pollution emitted

🔑 **Connect It** If you are a scientist inventing a solar powered car, what would you tell people about your invention so they would invest money in its development?

__Accept all reasonable responses. Sample answer: A solar powered car is an important__

__invention because it uses a completely free and renewable resource, sunlight.__

__Because the car does not burn fossil fuels, it does not pollute the atmosphere.__

Chapter Wrap-Up

Now that you have read the chapter, think about what you have learned.

Use this checklist to help you study.

❏ Complete your Foldables® Chapter Project.

❏ Study your *Science Notebook* on this chapter.

❏ Study the definitions of vocabulary words.

❏ Reread the chapter, and review the charts, graphs, and illustrations.

❏ Review the Understanding Key Concepts at the end of each lesson.

❏ Look over the Chapter Review at the end of the chapter.

THE BIG IDEA **Summarize It** Reread the chapter Big Idea and the lesson Key Concepts. Summarize why it is important to include a lesson about human population in a chapter about the environment when the remaining three lessons are about land, water, and air. Why does it matter?

Accept all reasonable responses. Sample answer: Land, water, and air are all

elements of the environment that are impacted by the actions of humans. The

greater the human population, the more substantially human activity affects the

environment. Air, land, and water are all connected in processes that sustain life on

Earth. Damage to those systems affects the well being of many organisms,

including humans.

_____

_____

_____

_____

_____

_____

Challenge *Read a more detailed summary of the Kyoto Protocol. Do more research to learn about its supporters and its opponents. Make a table that lists the key arguments of both sides, and summarize your own opinion at the bottom of the page. Share your research with your class.*

Name _____   Date _____

Interactions of Human Body Systems

 ## How do human body systems interact and support life?

Before You Read

Before you read the chapter, think about what you know about the systems of the human body. Record three things that you already know about body systems in the first column. Then write three things that you would like to learn about the interaction of human body systems in the second column. Complete the final column of the chart when you have finished this chapter.

K What I Know	W What I Want to Learn	L What I Learned

Chapter Vocabulary

Lesson 1	Lesson 2
NEW macromolecule monosaccharide amino acid nucleotide	**NEW** homeostasis negative feedback positive feedback **REVIEW** cellular respiration **ACADEMIC** detect

A Lesson Content Vocabulary page for each lesson is provided in the Chapter Resources Files.

Scan *Lesson 1. Read the lesson titles and bold words. Look at the pictures. Identify three facts you discovered about the human body. Record your facts in your Science Journal.*

■ ■ ■ **Main Idea** ■ ■ ■   ■ ■ ■ ■ ■ ■ ■ ■ ■ ■ **Details** ■ ■ ■ ■ ■ ■ ■ ■ ■ ■

Life and Chemistry
I found this on page ____765____ .

Characterize *the process of chemical reaction.*

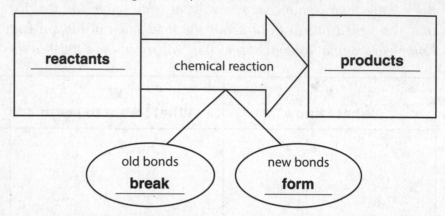

Elements and Compounds
I found this on page ____766____ .

Identify *elements that make up 99 percent of human body mass.*

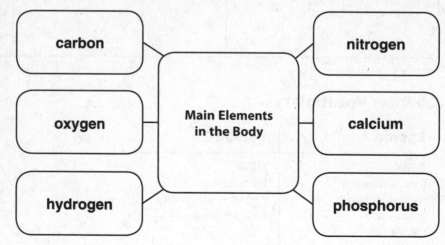

I found this on page ____766____ .

Contrast *two types of bonds.*

Ionic Bonds	Covalent Bonds
Form when **electrons travel from one element to another**	Form when **electrons in each element are shared**
Example: **table salt (NaCl)**	Example: **atmospheric gases such as oxygen (O_2) and nitrogen (N_2)**

Lesson 1 | The Human Body (continued)

<table>
<tr><td>

••• **Main Idea** •••

I found this on page ___767___ .

</td><td>

•••••••••• **Details** ••••••••••

Record *two details about inorganic compounds.*

1. **They do not contain carbon-hydrogen bonds.**

2. **Many are essential for human life.**

</td></tr>
</table>

I found this on page ___767___ .

🔑 **Characterize** *the importance of an inorganic ion.*

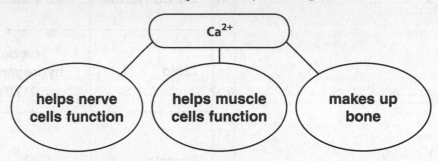

Ca²⁺

helps nerve cells function   helps muscle cells function   makes up bone

I found this on page ___767___ .

🔑 **Exemplify** *how water helps the body obtain organic substances. Use the dissolution of the ionic compound, table salt.*

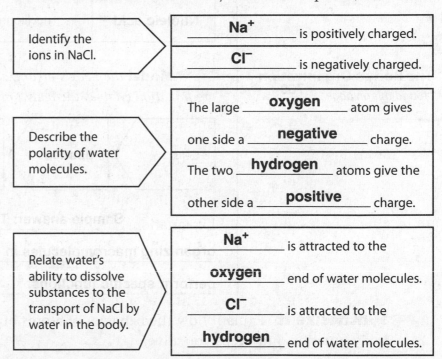

Identify the ions in NaCl.
— **Na⁺** — is positively charged.
— **Cl⁻** — is negatively charged.

Describe the polarity of water molecules.
The large — **oxygen** — atom gives one side a — **negative** — charge.
The two — **hydrogen** — atoms give the other side a — **positive** — charge.

Relate water's ability to dissolve substances to the transport of NaCl by water in the body.
— **Na⁺** — is attracted to the — **oxygen** — end of water molecules.
— **Cl⁻** — is attracted to the — **hydrogen** — end of water molecules.

I found this on page ___768___ .

Record *two details about organic compounds.*

1. **They contain carbon and other elements held together by covalent bonds.**

2. **Many are made by the human body to carry out different functions.**

Lesson 1 | The Human Body (continued)

▪▪▪ Main Idea ▪▪▪

I found this on page __768__ .

▪▪▪▪▪▪▪▪▪▪ Details ▪▪▪▪▪▪▪▪▪▪

🗝 **Differentiate** *details about 4 organic* macromolecules *in the body.*

Type	Made from	Details
Carbohydrate	monosaccharides	Examples: **sugars, starches, cellulose**
Lipid	**carbon, hydrogen, and oxygen**	Examples: **some hormones, cholesterol, triglycerides**
Protein	amino acids	Functions: **give cells structure, help cells communicate**
Nucleic acid	nucleotides	Examples: **DNA and RNA**

The Body's Organization

I found this on page __769__ .

🗝 **Model** *the body's organization, and then explain how this organization enables the body to function.*

Cells ⟩ **tissues** ⟩ **organs** ⟩ **organ systems**

Explanation: **Sample answer: The body functions by organizing macromolecules in specific locations that perform specific functions.**

🗝 **Synthesize It** Explain how the behavior of atoms of different elements helps your body function and keeps you alive.

Accept all reasonable responses. Sample answer: Atoms of different elements join to form molecules and compounds. Their bonds can be broken and new compounds formed. The body uses elements, ions, and compounds to build macromolecules. The macromolecules form different parts of cells, which form tissues, organs, and organ systems. The body continually uses organic and inorganic compounds.

Lesson 2 How Body Systems Interact

> **Predict** three facts that will be discussed in Lesson 2 after reading the headings. Write your facts in your Science Journal.

••• Main Idea ••• | ••••••••••••••• Details •••••••••••••••

Homeostasis
I found this on page ___773___ .

Sequence *the body's process for maintaining temperature.*

1	Body temperature falls.
2	Endocrine system: **sends a message through the nervous system**
3	Nervous system: **signals the muscle system to move**
4	You shiver.
5	Muscle movement: **generates thermal energy**
6	Body temperature rises.

I found this on page ___773___ .

Identify *five examples of* homeostasis *that the body's organ systems maintain.*

1. _____temperature_____   4. _____nutrient levels_____
2. _____oxygen_____   5. _____fluid levels_____
3. _____pH_____

Processing Nutrients

🔑 **Relate** *parts of body systems to their roles in digestion.*

Parts	What they do
Muscles in the jaw	**move the jaw to enable chewing and help you swallow**
Muscles around the esophagus, stomach, and intestines	**contract to move food through the digestive system**
Villi	**project into the small intestine; contain blood vessels**
Blood vessels	**transport nutrients throughout the body**

I found this on page ___774___ .
I found this on page ___774___ .
I found this on page ___775___ .
I found this on page ___775___ .

▪▪▪ **Main Idea** ▪▪▪

▪▪▪▪▪▪▪▪▪▪▪ **Details** ▪▪▪▪▪▪▪▪▪▪▪

Processing Oxygen and Wastes
I found this on page ____776____ .

🔑 **Relate** *parts of body systems to roles in oxygen transport.*

Parts	What they do
Muscular system	expands chest so lungs fill with air
Alveoli	contain capillaries inside the lungs
Capillaries	takes oxygen from air in the lungs into the bloodstream
Larger blood vessels	transport oxygen throughout the body

I found this on page ____777____ .

🔑 **Distinguish** *roles of body systems in removing wastes.*

Excretory System	Circulatory System	Respiratory System
removes feces through the rectum, liquid via urine through the kidneys, and sweat through the skin	removes carbon dioxide from tissues and transports it back to the lungs	removes carbon dioxide from the body as it is exhaled from the lungs

Control and Coordination
I found this on page ____778____ .

🔑 **Describe** *the sensory response shown in the pictures. Label the images with numbers from their corresponding descriptions in the table.*

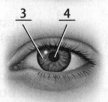

	In dim light
1	The iris contracts.
2	The pupil expands.
	In bright light
3	The iris expands.
4	The pupil contracts.

System that coordinates response to external stimuli: **nervous**

Lesson 2 | How Body Systems Interact (continued)

▪▪▪ Main Idea ▪▪▪ | ▪▪▪▪▪▪▪▪▪▪▪▪▪ Details ▪▪▪▪▪▪▪▪▪▪▪▪▪

I found this on page ___779___ .

🔑 **Record** *three characteristics of reflexes.*

1. rapid response

2. do not involve the brain

3. coordinated by the nervous system

I found this on page ___779___ .

🔑 **Differentiate** *how systems control responses.*

System	Type of Signal Used
Nervous	electrical signals
Endocrine	chemical signals

Feedback Mechanisms
I found this on page ___780___ .

🔑 **Contrast** *feedback mechanisms.*

Negative Feedback	Positive Feedback
Definition: **control system that sends a signal to stop a response**	Definition: **control system that sends a signal to increase a response**
Example: **end of hungry feeling after eating**	Example: **contractions during childbirth**

Students might also list blood clotting as an example of positive feedback.

🔑 **Connect It** Evaluate how body systems work together to get you through a school day.

Accept all reasonable responses. Sample answer: My respiratory and circulatory

systems work together all day to supply my body with oxygen and remove carbon

dioxide. My nervous and muscular systems allow me to move around and take in

sights and sounds. My digestive system, with the help of my circulatory and

excretory systems, processes my breakfast and lunch.

Chapter Wrap-Up

Now that you have read the chapter, think about what you have learned. Complete the final column in the chart on the first page of this chapter.

Use this checklist to help you study.

❏ Complete your Foldables® Chapter Project.

❏ Study your *Science Notebook* on this chapter.

❏ Study the definitions of vocabulary words.

❏ Reread the chapter, and review the charts, graphs, and illustrations.

❏ Review the Understanding Key Concepts at the end of each lesson.

❏ Look over the Chapter Review at the end of the chapter.

 Summarize It Reread the chapter Big Idea and the lesson Key Concepts. Summarize what you learned about how the body's systems use substances and work together to maintain homeostasis. Connect the concepts of Lesson 1 and Lesson 2.

Accept all reasonable responses. Sample answer: The body must maintain fairly

constant internal conditions despite its changing internal and external

environments. The body's ability to take in, transport, process, and recombine

substances, according to how those substances behave chemically, is what allows

us to stay alive. No one body system can manage all of the functions necessary to

maintain homeostasis. The systems work together to react to both the internal and

external environments in order to maintain homeostasis.

Challenge *Choose a substance that is required by the human body in order to stay alive. Research the chemical and physical properties of the substance. Find out how the body acquires the substance, how it transports and processes the substance, and for what purpose. Write a summary of your analysis. Include an explanation of what happens to the body if it has too little of the substance.*

Name _____ Date _____

Heredity and How Traits Change

 How do species adapt to new environments over time?

Before You Read

Before you read the chapter, think about what you know about heredity. Record three things that you already know about heredity in the first column. Then write three things that you would like to learn about how traits change in the second column. Complete the final column of the chart when you have finished the chapter.

K What I Know	W What I Want to Learn	L What I Learned

Chapter Vocabulary

Lesson 1	Lesson 2	Lesson 3
NEW heredity genetics selective breeding dominant trait recessive trait genotype phenotype heterozygous homozygous **REVIEW** trait	**NEW** monohybrid cross Punnett square incomplete dominance codominance multiple alleles sex-linked trait polygenic inheritance pedigree mutation genetic engineering	**NEW** variation natural selection adaptation evolution extinction conservation biology **ACADEMIC** survive

A Lesson Content Vocabulary page for each lesson is provided in the Chapter Resources Files.

Scan *Lesson 1. Read the lesson titles and bold words. Look at the pictures. Identify three facts you discovered about how traits are inherited. Record your facts in your Science Journal.*

••• **Main Idea** •••

From Parent to Offspring
I found this on page __793__ .

How are traits inherited?
I found this on page __794__ .

Why do scientists study genetics?
I found this on page __795__ .

Heredity—the History and the Basics
I found this on page __796__ .

•••••• **Details** ••••••

Diagram *definitions of* heredity *and* genetics.

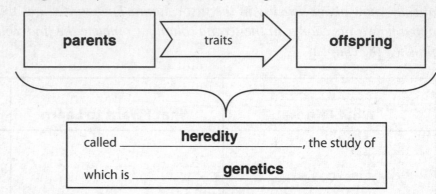

| parents | traits | offspring |

called __heredity__ , the study of
which is __genetics__

🔑 **Categorize** *the passage of traits to offspring.*

Source	Process	Result
Genes of one organism	**asexual reproduction**	Offspring: a copy of parent organism's genes and traits
Genes from: **an egg and a sperm**	sexual reproduction	Offspring: **inherits half its genes from each parent**
Environment	learning	**acquired traits**

🔑 **Identify** *three reasons why scientists study* genetics.

1. to learn how organisms develop
2. to learn how some diseases develop
3. to learn how species are related

Record *the meaning of* selective breeding.
the selection and breeding of organisms for desired traits

Lesson 1 | How are traits inherited? (continued)

▪▪▪ **Main Idea** ▪▪▪

I found this on page _____796_____ .

The green-pod parent is green; the yellow-pod parent is yellow; the four hybrid offspring are green.

I found this on page _____797_____ .

Both hybrid parents are green; three crossed hybrid offspring are green (dominant), and one is yellow (recessive).

I found this on page _____798_____ .

I found this on page _____798_____ .

▪▪▪▪▪▪ **Details** ▪▪▪▪▪▪

🔑 **Model** *Mendel's breeding experiments. Color-code parents and offspring in green and yellow. Identify the* dominant trait *and the* recessive trait *in the crossed hybrids.*

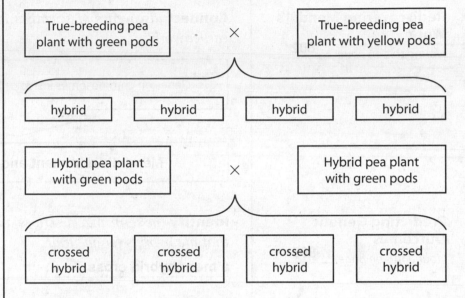

Relate *genotype to* phenotype.

| Genotype
the alleles of all the genes on an organism's chromosomes | Phenotype
how traits appear or are expressed |

Differentiate *heterozygous and* homozygous *traits.*

Trait	Description of Alleles
Heterozygous	**two different alleles for a trait**
Homozygous	**two identical alleles for a trait**

🔑 **Analyze It** If the dominant allele for fur color is purple and the recessive allele for fur color is green, what can you say about the alleles of an animal with green fur?

Accept all reasonable responses. Sample answer: The animal does not have a

purple-fur allele. If it did, that would be the dominant allele, it would cancel out the

green-fur trait, and the trait of purple fur would be expressed.

Lesson 2 Genetics After Mendel

Predict *three facts that will be discussed in Lesson 2 after reading the headings. Write your facts in your Science Journal.*

▪▪▪ Main Idea ▪▪▪ | ▪▪▪▪▪▪▪▪ Details ▪▪▪▪▪▪▪▪

Rediscovering Mendel's Work

I found this on page ____802____ .

Connect *discoveries of scientists in the early 1900s to Mendel's earlier work.*

> Genes on chromosomes inside cell nucleus are responsible for

⬇

> **Mendel's dominant and recessive factors.**

Predicting Genetic Outcomes

I found this on page ____803____ .

I found this on page ____803____ .

Identify *the term that describes a cross between two individuals that are hybrids for one trait.*

a monohybrid cross

🗝 **Complete** *and interpret* two Punnett squares *for plants where* **C** *indicates curled leaves and* **c** *indicates flat leaves.*

1.

	C	c
c	Cc	cc
c	Cc	cc

2.

	C	c
C	CC	Cc
c	Cc	cc

Questions	Square 1	Square 2
1. How many parents are heterozygous?	1	2
2. How many parents have curled leaves?	1	2
3. What percent of offspring will have curled leaves?	50	75
4. What percent of offspring express the recessive phenotype?	50	25
5. What percent of offspring are homozygous?	50	50

▪▪▪ **Main Idea** ▪▪▪ | ▪▪▪▪▪▪▪▪▪▪▪ **Details** ▪▪▪▪▪▪▪▪▪▪▪

Other Patterns of Inheritance
I found this on page ___804___ .

🔑 **Distinguish** *terms associated with patterns of inheritance.*

Term	Description
Incomplete dominance	**An offspring's phenotype is a combination of its parents' phenotypes.**
Codominance	**Both alleles can be independently observed in a phenotype.**
Multiple alleles	**a gene that has more than two alleles**

I found this on page ___805___ .

🔑 **Assess** *why alleles on X and Y chromosomes are called* sex-linked traits.

because X and Y chromosomes determine an organism's

gender

I found this on page ___805___ .

🔑 **Describe** polygenic inheritance, *and cite three examples.*

Polygenic Inheritance
Description: **occurs when multiple genes determine the phenotype of a trait**

Sample examples are shown.

| **human height** | **number of petals on a daisy** | **length of flowers on tomato plants** |

Lesson 2 | Genetics After Mendel (continued)

■■■ **Main Idea** ■■■	■■■■■■■■ **Details** ■■■■■■■■

Inheritance of Disease
I found this on page ___806___ .

Interpret *a* pedigree.

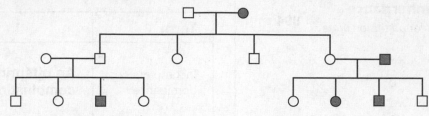

1. How many generations are shown?	**3**
2. How many offspring have the first-generation parents produced?	**4**
3. How many second-generation offspring have reproduced?	**2**
4. How many offspring do each of the second-generation parents have?	**4**
5. How many individuals display the recessive trait?	**5**
6. Are the total numbers of males and females equal?	**yes**

I found this on page ___806___ .

🔑 **Relate** mutation *to disease.*

Mutation permanent change in the sequence of DNA in a gene or a chromosome	⟹	Can cause: **change in appearance or function of an organism** Examples: **cancer, diabetes, birth defects**

I found this on page ___807___ .

Sample answer is shown.

Identify *a beneficial use of* genetic engineering.

Bacteria can be engineered to produce human insulin for

use by people with diabetes.

🔑 **Connect It** Look at the traits of all of the people around you. Summarize why there are so many variations of eye, skin, and hair color and other phenotypes.

Accept all reasonable responses. Sample answer: Many traits combine to form a

person's appearance. Dominance, incomplete dominance, multiple alleles, and

polygenic inheritance of traits produce such a complex variety of combinations that

no two individual human beings share the same combined phenotype unless they are

identical twins (or other identical multiples).

Lesson 3 Adaptation and Evolution

Skim *Lesson 3 in your book. Read the headings and look at the photos and illustrations. Identify three things you want to learn more about as you read the lesson. Record your ideas in your Science Journal.*

▪▪▪ **Main Idea** ▪▪▪

Mutations, Variation, and Natural Selection

I found this on page ___811___ .

I found this on page ___812___ .

I found this on page ___812___ .

Sample answer is shown. Students might also describe the sunflower example or others.

▪▪▪▪▪▪▪▪▪▪ **Details** ▪▪▪▪▪▪▪▪▪▪

Identify *three examples of* variation *in birds.*

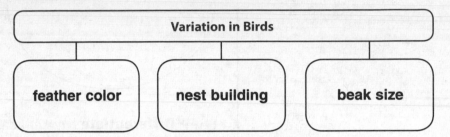

Variation in Birds
- feather color
- nest building
- beak size

Diagram *the concept of* natural selection.

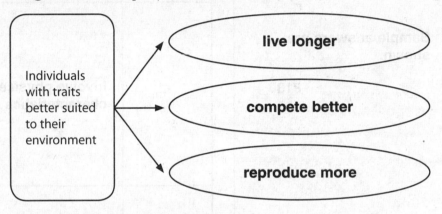

Individuals with traits better suited to their environment
- live longer
- compete better
- reproduce more

🔑 **Sequence** *an example of* natural selection.

1. Variation: **Some finches have larger beaks than others.**

2. Inheritance: **Larger-beaked finches produce offspring with larger beaks.**

3. Competition: **Finches with larger beaks better survive a drought that changes the type of food available.**

4. Natural selection: **Surviving finches pass on the large beak trait to their offspring; average beak size of the population increases.**

▪▪▪ **Main Idea** ▪▪▪ | ▪▪▪▪▪▪▪▪ **Details** ▪▪▪▪▪▪▪▪

Adaptations

I found this on page ___**813**___ .

Distinguish adaptation *from* variation.

Variation

slight differences in traits among a population

Adaptation

an inherited trait that increases an organism's chance of surviving and reproducing

 Differentiate *types of* adaptations.

Type	Description	Example
Structural	involve physical characteristics	Small leaves on a cactus help reduce water loss in a dry environment.
Functional	internal systems that affect an organism's physiology or biochemistry	Snowbells produce dormant flower buds at the end of one season that bloom at the beginning of the next season.
Behavioral	ways an organism behaves or acts	Groups of animals migrate to find adequate food and suitable temperatures.

Sample answers are shown.

I found this on page ___**813**___ .

I found this on page ___**814**___ .

I found this on page ___**814**___ .

▪▪▪ **Main Idea** ▪▪▪ | ▪▪▪▪▪▪▪▪▪▪▪▪ **Details** ▪▪▪▪▪▪▪▪▪▪▪▪▪

Evolution of Populations—Why Traits Change

I found this on page _____815_____ .

🔑 **Evaluate** *the cause and effect of* evolution *in a population. Relate the example of bacteria in the second diagram.*

The _____ environment changes.	→	Natural _____ selection occurs.	→	Result: **surviving breeding population** differs from _____ **ancestors**
Some bacteria have a mutation that enables them to survive antibiotics.	→	The surviving bacteria pass that trait to their offspring.	→	Result: **Most of the individuals in the population are antibiotic-resistant.**

Extinction and Conservation Biology

I found this on page _____816_____ .

Identify *three factors that can threaten a species with* extinction.

1. altered or destroyed habitat _____

2. hunting _____

3. introduction of new species _____

I found this on page _____816_____ .

Explain *how relocating female panthers from Texas to Florida represents an example of* conservation biology.

Conservation biologists moved the panthers to try to help

save the Florida species that was in trouble. The breeding

of the relocated panthers reintroduced more diversity to a

population in danger of extinction.

🔑 **Synthesize It** Habitat destruction can lead to an animal population's extinction. Describe one example of how a factor could be human-caused and one example of how this same factor could be caused by a natural event.

Accept all reasonable responses. Sample answer: Clearing of forest land to build

developments removes the habitat of animals that then have no place to find food or

shelter. A natural disaster such as a volcanic eruption, might also destroy a forested

area, leaving animals with no food or shelter.

Heredity and How Traits Change

Chapter Wrap-Up

Now that you have read the chapter, think about what you have learned. Complete the final column in the chart on the first page of the chapter.

Use this checklist to help you study.

❏ Complete your Foldables® Chapter Project.

❏ Study your *Science Notebook* on this chapter.

❏ Study the definitions of vocabulary words.

❏ Reread the chapter, and review the charts, graphs, and illustrations.

❏ Review the Understanding Key Concepts at the end of each lesson.

❏ Look over the Chapter Review at the end of the chapter.

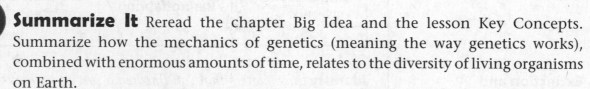 **Summarize It** Reread the chapter Big Idea and the lesson Key Concepts. Summarize how the mechanics of genetics (meaning the way genetics works), combined with enormous amounts of time, relates to the diversity of living organisms on Earth.

Accept all reasonable responses. Sample answer: Organisms pass on traits to their

offspring. The environments in which organisms live change over time. Organisms

with traits that enable them to survive an environmental change are the ones that

survive to reproduce and pass on their traits. Long periods of time see many

changes in the environments of the many different habitats on Earth. The

combination of many changes to many environments over a length of time has

produced variety, or diversity, in living organisms.

Challenge *Find material to read about the Galapagos Islands. Learn why the Galapagos have been so important to the study of variation, adaptation, natural selection and evolution. Write a report that summarizes what you learn.*

Copyright © Glencoe/McGraw-Hill, a division of The McGraw-Hill Companies, Inc.